Isaac Physics Skills

Linking concepts in
pre-university physics

Lisa Jardine-Wright, Keith Dalby, Robin Hughes, Nicki Humphry-Baker,
Anton Machacek, Ingrid Murray and Lee Phillips
Isaac Physics Project

Periphyseos Press
Cambridge, UK.

Periphyseos Press
Cambridge

Cavendish Laboratory
J. J. Thomson Avenue, Cambridge CB3 0HE, UK

Published in the United Kingdom by Periphyseos Press, Cambridge
www.periphyseos.org.uk

Linking concepts in pre-university physics
Creative Commons Licence

The content of *Linking concepts in pre-university physics* is licensed under a
Attribution-ShareAlike 4.0 International (CC BY-SA 4.0) licence.

First published & First reprint 2022

Printed and bound in the UK by Short Run Press Limited, Exeter.

Typeset in $\LaTeX$

A catalogue record for this publication is available from the British Library

ISBN 978-1-8382160-6-1 Paperback

Use this collection of worksheets in parallel with the electronic version at
http://isaacphysics.org/books/linking_concepts. Marking of answers
and compilation of results is free on Isaac Physics. Register as a student or as a
teacher to gain full functionality and support.

used with kind permission of M. J. Rutter.

Linking Concepts – Notes for the Student and the Teacher

A basketball player trains for matches using fitness exercises and ball drills. A musician will play hours of scales, arpeggios and technical exercises in the course of achieving concert standard. In a similar way, a scientist, engineer or mathematician is able to solve problems in a creative way partly because they have practised with simpler questions.

Our book *Mastering Essential Pre-University Physics* contained many questions allowing students to practise applying a single concept of Physics to a variety of situations. However practice of this kind is not enough to solve the problems faced in professional life, advanced study, or even in an examination. For these, knowledge and understanding of different concepts need to be brought together to solve the problem. Furthermore, it is not always clear which prior knowledge is going to be helpful for a particular situation.

A member of our team noticed something which helped with revision for University exams; namely that questions often required particular concepts to be combined in similar ways. He made a list of the combinations, and the equations which could be obtained by putting those ideas together. He then practised these, and found it made facing the hard, novel questions in the exam more accessible, as there would always be something similar to one of the links he had practised. A similar approach works in pre-university study.

In this book you will find, on each double page spread, a particular link between Physics concepts (or between Physics and Mathematics). You will put the equations of the concepts together, and then apply this understanding to a variety of similar questions. By the end of the two pages, if you have done the questions, you should have no difficulty remembering the link and how to apply it.

We have three particular pieces of advice. Work through enough questions until the method of combining the concepts becomes second nature. Each time you start a new question, make the links afresh — do not copy out any algebraic derivation of a previous question. Instead, work from your fundamental equations (such as those which might be found on a data sheet) each time. This builds proficiency. Finally, in the run up to examinations, redo the first question from each double page spread to ensure that your knowledge of the links is sound. This is the equivalent of practising a bounce pass or an arpeggio.

Worked solutions to the first question in each section are given in the appendix of the book.

Isaac Physics Team
Cambridge, 2022

Contents

1 Gravitational potential and kinetic energy

Objects rising and falling exchange stores of gravitational potential and kinetic energy.

Example context: We can calculate the speed of objects after they have fallen. We can also work out the height to which a projected object rises. The analysis is particularly useful when balls bounce.

Quantities: h_0 starting height (m) v_0 starting speed $(\mathrm{m\,s}^{-1})$
h_1 final height (m) v_1 final speed $(\mathrm{m\,s}^{-1})$
m mass (kg) g gravitational field strength $(\mathrm{N\,kg}^{-1})$
E_K kinetic energy (J) E_{GP} gravitational potential energy (J)
η efficiency (no unit) E_T total energy (J)

Equations: $E_K = \frac{1}{2}mv^2$ $E_{GP} = mgh$ $E_T = E_K + E_{GP}$ $E_{T,\,after} = \eta E_{T,\,before}$

1.1   In the absence of air resistance, use the equations to derive expressions for

     a) the speed v_1 at the ground if an object was dropped from h_0,

     b) the speed v_1 at a height h_1 if an object had speed v_0 at h_0,

     c) the greatest height h_1 for an object projected up from the ground with speed v_0,

     d) the greatest height h_1 for an object projected up from a height h_0 with speed v_0,

     e) the greatest height h_1 above a hard surface reached by an object dropped from height h_0 if the efficiency of the bounce is η,

     f) the speed v_1 just after a bounce from a hard surface if the speed just before was v_0,

---

Example 1 – A 0.80 kg melon falls from 3.4 m. Calculate its speed just before striking the ground.

At start: $E_{T,before} = E_{GP,before} = mgh_0 = 0.800 \times 9.81 \times 3.4 = 26.68$ J.

At end: $E_{T,after} = E_{K,after} = \frac{1}{2}mv_1^2 = \frac{1}{2} \times 0.800 \times v_1^2 = 0.400v_1^2$.

$E_{T,before} = E_{T,after} \rightarrow 26.68 = 0.400\,v_1^2 \rightarrow v_1 = \sqrt{\dfrac{26.68}{0.400}} = 8.2\ \mathrm{m\,s}^{-1}.$

1.2   An 800 kg pumpkin falls from 3.4 m. Calculate its speed just before striking the ground.

1.3 A 60 g tennis ball is hit upwards at 27 m s^{-1}. How high will it rise?

1.4 A 60 g tennis ball is hit upwards at 27 m/s from a 25 m high rooftop. How fast will it be travelling when it passes the rooftop on the way down?

Example 2 – *Calculate the height reached by a 0.15 kg ball thrown up from a 20 m cliff with a speed of 15 m s^{-1}.*

$$E_{T,before} = E_{GP,before} + E_{K,before} = mgh_0 + \tfrac{1}{2}mv_0^2$$
$$= 0.15 \times 9.81 \times 20 + \tfrac{1}{2} \times 0.15 \times 15^2 = 46.31 \text{ J}$$
$$E_{T,after} = E_{GP,after} + E_{K,after} = mgh_1 + 0$$
$$= 0.15 \times 9.81 \times h_1 = 1.472\,h_1$$
$$E_{T,after} = E_{T,before} \rightarrow 1.472\,h_1 = 46.31 \rightarrow h_1 = \frac{46.31}{1.472} = 32 \text{ m}$$

1.5 A 3.1 kg brick falls from scaffolding on a building site. A worker 3.5 m above the ground sees it fall past at 6.5 m/s. What is its kinetic energy just before striking the ground?

1.6 At what speed will a 4.2 kg lump of clay hit a potter's wheel if it is thrown downwards at 1.1 m s^{-1} from a height 40 cm above the wheel?

1.7 A worker at ground level throws a 2.2 kg drinks bottle upwards to a thirsty colleague 3.2 m above the ground. It just reaches him, but he fails to catch it, and it falls into an excavated trench 1.6 m below ground level.

   a) At what speed did the worker need to throw the bottle if she threw it from the waist, 1.0 m above the ground?

   b) How fast was it moving when it struck the base of the trench?

Example 3 – *A 25 g ball is thrown down to a hard surface at 12.3 m s^{-1}. How high will it rise after bouncing if $\eta = 0.35$?*
On hitting the surface $E_{T,before} = \tfrac{1}{2}mv_0^2 = \tfrac{1}{2} \times 0.025 \times 12.3^2 = 1.891$ J
$E_{T,after} = \eta E_{T,before} = 0.35 \times 1.891 = 0.6619$ J
$E_{T,after} = E_{GP,final} = mgh_1 = 0.025 \times 9.81 \times h_1 = 0.2453\,h_1$
So $0.6619 = 0.2453\,h_1 \rightarrow h_1 = \dfrac{0.6619}{0.2453} = 2.699$ m

---

1.8 A 5.2 g ball is dropped from 90 cm onto a surface and bounces to a maximum height of 41 cm. Calculate the efficiency η.

1.9 How fast would the ball in question 1.8 rebound if it struck the surface at 2.5 m s^{-1}?

1.10 How high would a ball bounce if it struck an $\eta = 0.75$ surface at 13 m s^{-1}?

2 Gravitational, elastic and kinetic energy

Objects suspended from a spring exchange stores of kinetic, elastic potential and kinetic energy as they move up and down.

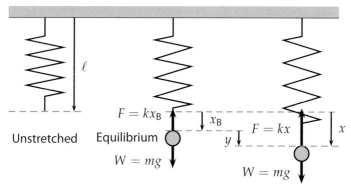

Quantities:

x spring extension (m)	ℓ spring natural length (m)
x_B equilibrium x (m)	y distance from equilibrium (m)
v speed $(\mathrm{m\,s^{-1}})$	k spring constant $(\mathrm{N\,m^{-1}})$
m mass (kg)	g gravitational field strength $(\mathrm{N\,kg^{-1}})$
E_K kinetic energy (J)	E_{GP} gravitational potential energy (J)
E_T total energy (J)	E_{EP} elastic potential energy (J)
F spring tension (N)	W weight (N)

Equations:
$$E_K = \tfrac{1}{2}mv^2 \quad E_{GP} = -mgx \quad E_{EP} = \tfrac{1}{2}kx^2 \quad F = kx$$
$$E_T = E_K + E_{GP} + E_{EP} \qquad W = mg \qquad y = x - x_B$$

2.1 In the absence of air resistance, use the equations to derive expressions for

   a) the total energy E_T in terms of x and v,

   b) the value of x where the forces balance (we will call this x_B),

   c) $E_{GP} + E_{EP}$ at the point where the forces balance (we will call this E_B),

   d) the greatest value of x if you hold the mass at $x = 0$ and let it go,

   e) (optional) the value of $E_{GP} + E_{EP}$ in terms of $y = x - x_B$.

2.2 Calculate E_{GP}, E_{EP}, E_K and E_T for a 2.5 kg mass when $x = 0.055$ m and $v = 0.25\ \mathrm{m\,s^{-1}}$ if $k = 600\ \mathrm{N\,m^{-1}}$.

2.3 Calculate x_B (the extension of the spring at the equilibrium point) for a 100 N weight hanging from a $k = 5000\ \mathrm{N\,m^{-1}}$ spring.

> **Example** – *A 60 kg bungee jumper falls 12 m before their bungee is taut. How fast will they be moving after falling a further 4.0 m?* $k = 200\,N\,m^{-1}$
> At the start $x = -12$ m and $v = 0$, and $E_K = E_{EP} = 0$,
> so $E_T = E_{GP} = -mgx = -60 \times 9.81 \times (-12) = 7063$ J.
> When $x = 4.0$ m, $E_T = E_{EP} + E_{GP} + E_K = \frac{1}{2}kx^2 - mgx + \frac{1}{2}mv^2$
> so $E_T = \frac{1}{2} \times 200 \times 4^2 - 60 \times 9.81 \times 4 + \frac{1}{2} \times 60 \times v^2$
> and so $E_T = -754.4 + 30v^2$.
> Total energy is constant so $7063 = -754.4 + 30v^2$,
> therefore $7817.4 = 30v^2$ and $v = \sqrt{\dfrac{7817.4}{30}} = 16\ m\,s^{-1}$

2.4 Calculate the speed of the bungee jumper in the example when

      a) the bungee has stretched 5.0 m,

      b) the bungee becomes slack on the way up.

2.5 Fill in the missing entries in the table below. This describes the motion of a 100 N weight ($m = 10.2$ kg), hanging from a $k = 5000\,N\,m^{-1}$ spring, which is released from rest at $x = 0$. You calculated x_B in question 2.3.

x	v	E_K	E_{GP}	E_{EP}	$E_{EP} + E_{GP}$	E_T	$y = x - x_B$
/ cm	/ m s^{-1}			/J			/ cm
1.0	(a)	(b)	(c)	(d)	(e)	0.0	(f)
2.0	(g)	(h)	(i)	(j)	(k) = E_B	0.0	0.0
3.0	(l)	(m)	(n)	(o)	(p)	0.0	(q)
4.0	(r)	(s)	(t)	(u)	(v)	0.0	(w)

2.6 For the system in question 2.5, state or calculate

      a) the value of x where the total potential energy is a minimum,

      b) the minimum total potential energy,

      c) the total potential energy *relative to the minimum* when $y = 2.0$ cm,

      d) the energy required to stretch a $k = 5000\,N\,m^{-1}$ spring by 2.0 cm.

2.7 Calculate how far the bungee jumper in the example falls before they first come to rest. You may assume that the *total* potential energy of the jumper relative to the equilibrium position is given by $\frac{1}{2}ky^2$.

3 Momentum and kinetic energy

It is helpful to be able to calculate a momentum from a kinetic energy without first working out the speed.

Example context: In particle physics, the wavelength of a particle is related to its momentum. In a question you are more likely to be told its energy (eg. a 50 keV electron) than its speed.

Quantities:
p momentum (kg m s^{-1}) E kinetic energy (J)
m mass (kg) λ wavelength (m)
v speed (m s^{-1}) q charge (C)
V accelerating voltage (V) h Planck constant (J s)

Equations: $p = mv$ $E = \frac{1}{2}mv^2$ $E = qV$ $\lambda = \dfrac{h}{p}$

3.1   Use the equations to derive expressions without v for

     a) the kinetic energy E in terms of p and m,

     b) the momentum p in terms of E and m,

     c) the momentum of an accelerated particle in terms of V, m and q,

     d) the wavelength of an accelerated particle in terms of V and q.

Example 1 – *Calculate the kinetic energy of a 9 kg pumpkin with a momentum of 150 kg m s^{-1}.*

$$E = \frac{m}{2}v^2 = \frac{m}{2}\left(\frac{p}{m}\right)^2 = \frac{p^2}{2m} = \frac{150^2}{2 \times 9} = 1250 \text{ J}$$

Example 2 – *calculate the wavelength of a 1 keV electron.*
Kinetic energy $E = qV$ where q is the charge on one electron and $V = 1000$ V. As $E = \frac{1}{2}mv^2$, the momentum will be

$$p = mv = m\sqrt{\frac{2E}{m}} = \sqrt{2mE} = \sqrt{2mqV}, \text{ so we calculate } \lambda = \frac{h}{p} \text{ as}$$

$$\lambda = \frac{h}{\sqrt{2mqV}} = \frac{6.63 \times 10^{-34}}{\sqrt{2 \times 9.1 \times 10^{-31} \times 1.6 \times 10^{-19} \times 10^3}} = 3.89 \times 10^{-11} \text{ m}$$

3.2   Calculate the kinetic energy of a $p = 23\,700$ kg m s^{-1}, 720 kg car.

3.3　Fill in the missing entries in the table below.

Mass / kg	Momentum / kg m s^{-1}	Kinetic energy / J
32	(a)	0.040
5.6	252	(b)
4.6 g	(c)	980
12 000	168 000	(d)

3.4　Calculate the momentum of a 200 g orange with 54 J of kinetic energy.

3.5　Calculate the momentum of a proton accelerated by 20 kV.

3.6　Calculate the kinetic energy of a neutron with a wavelength of 2.4 nm.

3.7　Calculate the wavelength of an 80 keV electron.

3.8　Calculate the accelerating voltage needed to produce protons with a wavelength of 3.5 pm.

3.9　Calculate the wavelength of a 50 MeV proton.

3.10　Calculate the wavelength of a 10 MeV alpha particle.

3.11　A 10 MeV particle in a particle detector travels on a curved path in a magnetic field. Its charge is 1.60×10^{-19} C. From the curvature, the momentum of the particle is calculated to be 7.31×10^{-20} kg m s^{-1}.

　　a) What is the mass of the particle?

　　b) What is the particle?

3.12　A 15 g bullet hits and stops within a 1.500 kg sandbag, which then swings up by a height of 5.1 cm. Work out the initial speed of the bullet. Hint: the height can be used to work out the gravitational potential energy, and hence the initial kinetic energy of the bag. The momentum of the bag just after the collision will be equal to the momentum of the bullet before it.

4 Elastic collisions

An elastic collision is one where the total kinetic energy is the same before and after the collision. Momentum is also conserved (as in all collisions). Solving these questions needs energy and momentum formulae.

Example context: many collisions of subatomic particles are elastic, especially if the speeds aren't high enough to trigger reactions. Collisions between snooker balls are also almost elastic.

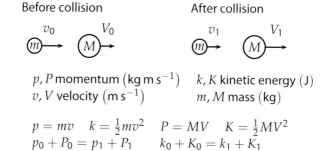

Quantities: p, P momentum (kg m s^{-1}) k, K kinetic energy (J)
v, V velocity (m s^{-1}) m, M mass (kg)

Equations: $p = mv$ $k = \frac{1}{2}mv^2$ $P = MV$ $K = \frac{1}{2}MV^2$
$p_0 + P_0 = p_1 + P_1$ $k_0 + K_0 = k_1 + K_1$

4.1   Use the equations to derive expressions for

a) the final velocity V_1 of M if M was stationary at the beginning and the initial and final velocities of m (v_0 and v_1) are known,

b) V_1 if the masses are equal $(M = m)$, M begins at rest $(V_0 = 0)$, m is stopped by the collision $(v_1 = 0)$ and v_0 is known,

c) (optional) $k + K$ in terms of $p + P$, M, m and the relative velocity $r = v - V$. Hint: use $2(m + M)$ as a denominator for $k + K$, and then look for terms adding to give $(p + P)^2$ on the top.

Example 1 – A 1 kg trolley moving at 1.2 m s^{-1} strikes a stationary 2 kg trolley, which then moves at 0.8 m s^{-1}. Calculate the final velocity of the 1 kg trolley.

$$mv_0 + MV_0 = mv_1 + MV_1 \text{ (conservation of momentum)}$$
$$1 \times 1.2 + 2 \times 0 = 1 \times v_1 + 2 \times 0.8$$
$$1.2 - 1.6 = v_1 \text{ and hence } v_1 = -0.4 \text{ m s}^{-1}$$

4.2   Calculate the kinetic energy lost by the 1 kg trolley in Example 1.

4.3   Calculate the final speed of the 2 kg trolley in Example 1 assuming that it gains all of the kinetic energy lost by the 1 kg trolley.

4.4 Fill in the missing entries in the table below. For these collisions $v_0 \neq v_1$.

m	M	v_0	V_0	v_1	V_1	$K+k$	$K_1 - K_0$
/kg			/m s^{-1}				/J
1.0	3.0	3.0	0.0	-1.5	(a)	(b)	(c)
0.050	0.050	1.5	0.0	0.0	(d)	(e)	(f)
2.0	3.0	3.0	(g)	(h)	(i)	15	0.0
0.010	0.99	50	0.0	(j)	1.0	(k)	(l)
0.010	9.99	50	0.0	(m)	0.10	(n)	(o)

4.5 In space, an elastic 'sling shot' collision is arranged between a stationary 6.4×10^{24} kg planet and a 6000 kg spacecraft moving at 4.5 km s^{-1}. By looking at the pattern in your answers to question 4.4 (j,m,l,o) estimate

    a) the kinetic energy gained by the planet,

    b) the final speed of the spacecraft.

In elastic collisions, the approach speed $|v_0 - V_0|$ and the separation speed $|V_1 - v_1|$ are equal. This is a consequence of question 4.1 part (c).

4.6 Repeat question 4.5b where the planet is also moving towards the spacecraft at 9.0 km s^{-1}.

> **Example 2** – A neutron m with $v_0 = 1200$ m s^{-1} collides elastically with a stationary hydrogen molecule $M = 2m$. Calculate the velocity of the molecule after the collision.
> The two particles must separate at v_0, so if the molecule's final velocity is V_1, $v_1 = V_1 - v_0$. Conservation of momentum gives $mv_0 + 0 = mv_1 + 2mV_1$, so $v_0 = (V_1 - v_0) + 2V_1$, so $2v_0 = 3V_1$, and $V_1 = \frac{2}{3}v_0 = 800$ m s^{-1}.

4.7 A neutron (of mass m) travelling at 2.4×10^5 m s^{-1} collides elastically with a stationary carbon nucleus (mass $M = 12m$).

    a) Calculate the final speed of the carbon nucleus.

    b) Calculate the percentage of the neutron's kinetic energy which is given to the nucleus.

4.8 Repeat question 4.7 for a neutron of the same speed colliding with an iron nucleus ($M = 65m$).

5 Vectors and motion – relative motion

It is helpful to be able to calculate the time it would take for two bodies to collide when they are travelling in the same direction, with the body in front is moving slower than the body behind.

Example context: Achilles chases after a tortoise. Achilles is faster than the tortoise; however, by the time Achilles reaches where the tortoise was, it has moved forwards. When will Achilles catch up with the tortoise?

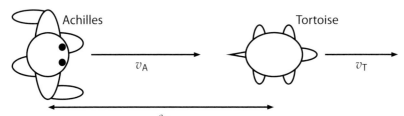

Quantities: v_A velocity of Achilles (m s^{-1}) s_0 initial displacement (m)
v_T velocity of tortoise (m s^{-1}) s displacement (m)
T time for Achilles to catch up (s) t time since start (s)

Equations: $v = \dfrac{s}{t}$

5.1   Use the equations to derive expressions for

    a) the velocity of Achilles relative to the Tortoise v_{REL},

    b) the time for Achilles to catch up with the tortoise T, in terms of v_A and v_T,

    c) the displacement of the tortoise relative to Achilles as a function of time s.

5.2   Fill in the missing entries in the table below, using the diagram and quantities above to help.

s_0 / m	v_A / m s^{-1}	v_T / cm s^{-1}	T / s
(a)	5.81	6.71	15.0
1000	(b)	7.50	136
500	1.34	(c)	400
250	5.50	3.42	(d)

> **Example 1** – *The tortoise hops on a motor cycle and can travel at* $18.0\ m\,s^{-1}$,
> *whereas Achilles can only run at* $12.4\ m\,s^{-1}$. *They are initially 50.0 m apart.*
> *Calculate the time taken for them to be 1.00 km apart.*
> $$s = s_0 - (v_A - v_T)\,t \text{ therefore } t = -\frac{s - s_0}{v_A - v_T} = -\frac{1000 - 50.0}{12.4 - 18.0} = 170\ s$$

5.3 Following on from **Example 1** above, when the tortoise travelling at $18.0\,\mathrm{m\,s^{-1}}$ is 1.00km away from Achilles, Achilles gets into a motor vehicle that can travel at $96.5\ \mathrm{km\,h^{-1}}$. Calculate how far ahead of the tortoise Achilles is after 2 minutes.

5.4 The tortoise and Achilles decide to participate in a jousting competition, whereupon the two charge at each other as fast as they can. They are initially stood 50.0 m apart from each other. The tortoise charges towards Achilles at $5.00\,\mathrm{m\,s^{-1}}$, and Achilles charges towards the tortoise at $15.0\,\mathrm{m\,s^{-1}}$. Calculate
    a) the time taken before they collide,

    b) how far Achilles has travelled when they collide.

> **Example 2** – *Achilles and the tortoise start at the same location. Achilles travels*
> *due South at* $15.0\ m\,s^{-1}$, *and the tortoise travels due East at* $8.00\ m\,s^{-1}$. *Calculate how far apart they will be after 10 s.*
> Tortoise moves $8.00\ \mathrm{m\,s^{-1}} \times 10\ s = 80\ m$ East.
> Achilles moves $15.0\ \mathrm{m\,s^{-1}} \times 10\ s = 150\ m$ South.
> Distance apart (using Pythagoras) $= \sqrt{150^2 + 80^2} = 170\ m$

5.5 Achilles starts 50.0 m due North of the tortoise. The tortoise runs due East at $3.00\,\mathrm{m\,s^{-1}}$. Achilles walks briskly at $4.24\ \mathrm{m\,s^{-1}}$ South-East. Calculate
    a) how long until Achilles intercepts the tortoise,

    b) How far Achilles has travelled in this time,

    c) How far the tortoise has travelled in this time.

5.6 Achilles starts 100.0 m due North of the tortoise. The tortoise runs due East at $2.50\ \mathrm{m\,s^{-1}}$. Achilles runs at $7.31\ \mathrm{m\,s^{-1}}$ on a bearing of $160°$. A squirrel starts 50.0 m due South of the tortoise and scurries due North at a speed of $8.90\ \mathrm{m\,s^{-1}}$. Calculate
    a) how long until Achilles intercepts the tortoise,

    b) the distance between Achilles and the squirrel when Achilles intercepts the tortoise.

6   Vectors and motion – projectiles

It is useful to be able to calculate the maximum height and range of a body projected diagonally.

Example context: a trebuchet launches a missile towards the walls of a castle. The missile is massive enough that air resistance can be neglected.

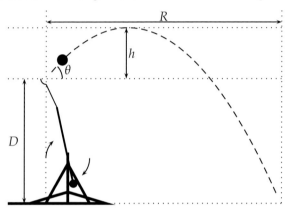

Quantities: u initial velocity $(\mathrm{m\,s^{-1}})$ v final velocity $(\mathrm{m\,s^{-1}})$
a acceleration $(\mathrm{m\,s^{-2}})$ R range of projectile (m)
s displacement (m) D initial vertical displacement (m)
t time (s) T time of flight (s)
h height increase (m) θ projection angle $(^{\circ})$
Subscripts $_x$ and $_y$ label horizontal and vertical components.

Equations: $v = u + at$ $s = \dfrac{v + u}{2}t$ $s = ut + \dfrac{1}{2}at^2$ $v^2 = u^2 + 2as$

6.1   Use the equations to derive expressions for

a) the height increase h,

b) the final vertical component of velocity $v_{\mathrm{y,final}}$ of the missile in terms of h,

c) the time of flight of the projectile T,

d) the range of the projectile R.

> **Example 1** – *The projectile is launched at an angle of 55.0° and with an initial velocity of 10.0 m s⁻¹ from a height of 4.00 m. What is the maximum height of the projectile above the ground?*
>
> Use $h = \dfrac{u^2 \sin^2 \theta}{2g} = \dfrac{10.0^2 \sin^2 55.0}{2 \times 9.81} = 3.42$ m,
>
> so maximum height $= D + h = 4.00 + 3.42 = 7.42$ m

6.2   Calculate the maximum height of a projectile launched from a trebuchet with the following initial values:

   a) $u = 22.0$ m s⁻¹ $@\,\theta = 45.0°$ from $s_y = 4.00$ m.

   b) $u = 15.5$ m s⁻¹ $@\,\theta = 40.0°$ from $s_y = 4.50$ m.

   c) $u = 10.5$ m s⁻¹ $@\,\theta = 55.0°$ from $s_y = 3.75$ m.

> **Example 2** – *Consider the same projectile as in **Example 1**. What is the vertical component of final velocity?*
>
> Use $v_y = \sqrt{2 \times g \times (D + h)}$ because at the highest point $u_y = 0$.
>
> $v_y = \sqrt{2 \times 9.81 \times (4.00 + 3.42)} = 12.1$ m s⁻¹   (12.07 m s⁻¹ to 4sf)

6.3   Calculate the vertical component of final velocity of the projectiles launched from a trebuchet with the same initial values as question 6.2:

> **Example 3** – *Consider the same projectile as in **Example 1**. What is the time of flight?*
>
> Use $t = \dfrac{v_y - u_y}{a_y} = \dfrac{12.07 + 10.0 \sin 55.0°}{9.81} = 2.07$ s   (2.065 s to 4sf)
>
> The positive sign is because the vertical components of the initial and final velocities are in opposite directions.

6.4   Calculate the time of flight of the projectiles launched from a trebuchet with the same initial values as question 6.2:

> **Example 4** – *Consider the same projectile as in **Example 1**. What is the horizontal range of the projectile?*
>
> Use $s_x = u_x t = u \cos \theta \times t = 10.0 \cos 55.0 \times 2.065 = 11.8$ m
>
> Note that the incorrect answer of 11.9 m is calculated if the rounded value $t = 2.07$ s is used.

6.5   Calculate the horizontal range of the projectiles launched from a trebuchet with the same initial values as question 6.2:

7   Photon flux for an LED

Photon flux (the number of photons per second) is closely related to intensity of light. Understanding how light is quantised and how current and photon flux are related in devices like LEDs and solar cells can be useful.

Example context: The energy levels in the material cause Light Emitting Diodes (LEDs) to emit light of particular wavelengths. The energy band levels correspond to the emitted photon energies, and therefore the wavelength of the emitted light. The potential difference across a component is how much energy per unit charge has been transferred by the component as the charge flows through it. Here we will assume that the drop in potential difference across an LED is entirely due to an electron changing energy state in the LED, releasing a photon in the process.

Quantities:　　Φ_q photon flux (s^{-1})　　　　　V potential difference (V)
　　　　　　　E photon energy (J)　　　　　　e electron charge (magnitude) (C)
　　　　　　　λ wavelength of light (m)　　　　P LED power (W)
　　　　　　　I electric current (A)　　　　　　n number of electrons or photons
　　　　　　　t duration (s)

Equations:　　$E = eV$　　$E = \dfrac{hc}{\lambda}$　　$\Phi_q = \dfrac{n}{t}$　　$ne = It$　　$P = IV$

7.1　　Use the equations to derive expressions for

　　　a) the current I in terms of Φ_q and e,

　　　b) the potential difference across a conducting LED V in terms of h, c, e, and λ,

　　　c) The power of the LED P in terms of h, c, λ, and Φ_q.

Example – *Calculate the current through an LED of power rating 88.8 mW that produces light of wavelength 700 nm.*

$$P = IV = I\frac{hc}{e\lambda} \quad \text{so} \quad \frac{e\lambda}{hc}P = I$$

$$I = \frac{Pe\lambda}{hc} = \frac{(8.88 \times 10^{-2})(1.60 \times 10^{-19})(7.00 \times 10^{-7})}{(6.63 \times 10^{-34})(3.00 \times 10^{8})} = 50.0 \text{ mA}$$

7.2 A 1.50 W Infra-Red LED produces electromagnetic radiation of wavelength 850 nm. Calculate

    a) the potential difference across the LED,

    b) the current that passes through the LED,

    c) the photon flux emitted by the LED.

7.3 A UV-C (ultra-violet) LED emits 1.00×10^{19} photons per second when there is a potential difference of 6.22 V across it. Calculate

    a) the current passing through the LED,

    b) the LED's power,

    c) the wavelength of electromagnetic radiation emitted.

7.4 Fill in the missing entries in the table below for different LEDs.

power P/mW	current I/mA	potential difference V/V	photon flux $\Phi_q/(10^{17}\mathrm{s}^{-1})$	wavelength λ/nm
	52.2		(a)	
75.0	(b)	2.26		(c)
	18.1	(d)	(e)	450
250	(f)	(g)	3.02	(h)

7.5 An LED has a power rating of 500 mW and produces blue light of wavelength 400 nm. Calculate

    a) the potential difference across the LED,

    b) the amount of charge that flows through the LED in one minute,

    c) the number of photons emitted in one minute.

7.6 An LED has a potential difference across it of 2.07 V and emits 2.72×10^{17} photons each second. Calculate

    a) the power of the LED,

    b) the amount of charge that flows through the LED each second,

    c) the amount of energy transferred by the LED in one hour.

8 Potential dividers with LEDs

It is helpful to be able to calculate the resistances necessary to obtain a particular output voltage from a potential divider circuit containing an LED.

Example context: this section builds on **Section 7** about photon flux by considering the LED in a circuit in series with a fixed resistor. The fixed resistor is needed to make sure the LED receives the correct current.

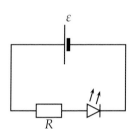

Quantities: ε e.m.f. (V)
V p.d. across fixed resistor (V)
V_{LED} p.d. across LED (V)
I current through circuit (A)
R fixed resistor resistance (Ω)
E photon energy (J)
λ wavelength of emitted light (m)

Equations: $\quad V = IR \quad \varepsilon = V_{LED} + V \quad V_{LED} = \dfrac{E}{e} \quad E = \dfrac{hc}{\lambda}$

8.1 Use the equations to derive expressions for

a) the resistance of the fixed resistor R in terms of the e.m.f. ε, the p.d. across the LED V_{LED} and the current I,

b) the resistance of the fixed resistor R in terms of the e.m.f. ε, the wavelength of the LED λ, the current I and the physical constants h, c and e.

8.2 Fill in the missing entries in the table below.

e.m.f. / V	current / mA	fixed resistor resistance / Ω	LED p.d. / V
9.00	12.1	(a)	4.14
6.00	(b)	300	1.78
(c)	8.05	73.6	3.11
5.00	10.1	250	(d)
7.40	51.5	(e)	2.25
12.0	28.8	330	(f)

> **Example 1** – *Calculate the resistance R needed when a 652 nm LED is connected to a 6.00 V battery if the current is to be 50.0 mA.*
>
> $$E = \frac{hc}{\lambda} = \frac{6.63 \times 10^{-34} \times 3.00 \times 10^8}{652 \times 10^{-9}} = 3.051 \times 10^{-19} \text{ J,}$$
>
> so $V_{LED} = \dfrac{E}{e} = 1.904$ V. $V = \varepsilon - V_{LED} = 6.00 - 1.90 = 4.10$ V
>
> $$R = \frac{V}{I} = \frac{4.10}{0.050} = 81.9 \ \Omega.$$

8.3   A blue LED produces light of wavelength 480 nm. It is powered using a 9.00 V battery using the circuit design shown above. Assume that there is no internal resistance in the power supply and calculate

       a) the p.d. across the LED,

       b) the minimum value of R to ensure the current through the LED does not exceed 50.0 mA,

       c) the resistance of the LED.

> **Example 2** – *Calculate the current through a 510 nm LED (with a p.d. of 2.44 V across it) connected to an e.m.f. of 5.00 V, in series with a 300 Ω resistor.*
>
> P.d. is shared, so p.d. across the resistor must be $5.00 - 2.44 = 2.56$ V
>
> Fixed resistor is ohmic, so use Ohm's law $I = \dfrac{V}{R} = \dfrac{2.56}{300} = 8.53$ mA
>
> As resistor and LED are in series, currents are the same.

8.4   A red LED produces light of wavelength 680 nm. It is powered using a 7.4 V battery with no internal resistance. Calculate

       a) the p.d. across the LED,

       b) the current through the LED when its power is 102 mW *(use $P = IV$)*,

       c) the resistance of the LED when its power is 102 mW,

       d) the resistance of the fixed resistor R.

8.5   Two LEDs *(labelled A and B)* are connected in parallel to a 3.7 V cell. Each LED is protected by its own resistor in series. *LED A* is protected by a 330 Ω resistor, whereas *LED B* is protected by a 165 Ω resistor. Both LEDs produce light of wavelength 650 nm. Presenting your answer as a decimal, calculate

       a) the ratio of the p.d. across *LED A* to the p.d. across *LED B*,

       b) the ratio of the current through *LED A* to the current through *LED B*,

9 Current division

It is helpful to be able to calculate the fraction of an electric current which takes each branch of a parallel circuit.

Example context: voltmeters are not perfect insulators. When the voltage across a component is measured, a fraction of the current flows through the voltmeter, and this affects the circuit. A knowledge of the fraction of current no longer flowing through the component enables a correction to be made.

Quantities: I current (A) V voltage (V)
                        R resistance (Ω) G conductance $(\Omega^{-1}$ or S$)$
                        Subscripts $_{1,2}$ label components. Subscript $_c$ refers to the circuit.

Equations: $R = \dfrac{V}{I}$ $G = \dfrac{I}{V} = \dfrac{1}{R}$ $R_{\text{parallel}} = \left(\dfrac{1}{R_1} + \dfrac{1}{R_2} + \cdots\right)^{-1}$
                    For components in parallel: $I_c = I_1 + I_2 + \ldots$ $V_1 = V_2 = \ldots$

9.1   Two resistors R_1 and R_2 are in parallel, and carry a total current I_c. Use the equations to write or derive expressions (in terms of I_c, R_1 and R_2) for

       a) the voltage V across each resistor,

       b) the current I_1 through resistor R_1,

       c) the fraction of the total current which flows through R_1: $\dfrac{I_1}{I_c}$,

       d) the conductance G_1 of resistor R_1,

       e) the total conductance $G_c = G_1 + G_2$ of the two resistors

       f) the fraction $\dfrac{G_1}{G_c}$.

Example – A 3.0 Ω resistor is wired in parallel with a 6.0 Ω resistor, and between them, they carry 24 mA. Calculate the current carried by the 6.0 Ω resistor.
Overall resistance $R_C = \left(3.0^{-1} + 6.0^{-1}\right)^{-1} = 2.0\,\Omega$
Voltage across combination $V = I_C R_C = 0.024 \times 2.0 = 0.048$ V
Current through the 6.0 Ω resistor $I_6 = \dfrac{V}{R} = \dfrac{0.048}{6} = 8.0$ mA

9.2   A 9.0 Ω resistor is connected in parallel with a 81 Ω resistor. What fraction of the total current flows through the 81 Ω resistor?

9.3   How much current flows through a 330 Ω resistor which is connected in parallel with a 68 Ω resistor which is carrying 40 mA by itself?

9.4   I am going to connect two resistors in parallel to share a 13 A current so that 5.0 A flows through one resistor. The resistor with the larger resistance is a 2.2 Ω resistor. Calculate the resistance of the other resistor.

9.5   Fill in the missing entries in the table below. In this circuit, three resistors (R_1, R_2, R_3) are connected in parallel.

R_1	R_2	R_3	I_1	I_2	I_3	I_C	V
/ Ω			/ A				/ V
1.0	2.0	3.0	(a)	(b)	(c)	2.4	(d)
5.0	15	20	(e)	(f)	(g)	(h)	12
48	(i)	7.5	5.0	20	(j)	(k)	(l)

9.6   A wire in an oven typically carries 20 A. I wish to put an LED in the circuit which will light up when the current is flowing. The LED requires a voltage of 1.8 V to light, and takes a current of 25 mA when it is lit. I will connect the LED in parallel with a resistor, and place the combination in series with the oven's heater element.

a) Calculate the resistance of the LED when it is lit.

b) Calculate the current through the resistor when the LED is lit.

c) Calculate the resistance of the resistor needed.

9.7   An ammeter designed for electricians has a resistance of 0.10 mΩ and it can measure a maximum of 200 A. I wish to adapt it so it can measure currents up to 1000 A by connecting a resistor in parallel with it.

a) What is the voltage across the ammeter when it carries 200 A?

b) Once the resistor is connected, what fraction of the total current should flow through the ammeter?

c) When the resistor is connected and the combination is carrying 1000 A, what is the current through the resistor?

d) Calculate the resistance of the resistor.

e) Using $P = IV$ calculate the power dissipated in the resistor when the combination is carrying 1000 A.

10   Power in a potential divider

It is helpful to be able to calculate the power (or fraction of the total power) dissipated in one part of a potential divider circuit.

Example context: Electrical generators have internal resistance. A power supply company wishes to maximise the efficiency of the system by ensuring that as much of the electricity generated as possible is passed on to customers.

Quantities: I current (A) P load power (W)
R load resistance (Ω) V voltage or p.d. across load (V)
r internal resistance (Ω) η efficiency (no unit)
ϵ electromotive force (emf) of supply (V)

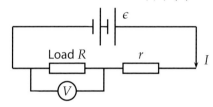

Equations: $P = IV = I^2R = \dfrac{V^2}{R}$ $V = IR$ $\epsilon = V + Ir$ $\eta = \dfrac{P}{I\epsilon}$

10.1   Use the equations to derive expressions for

    a) the current I in terms of ϵ, R and r,

    b) the load voltage V in terms of ϵ, R and r,

    c) the load power P in terms of ϵ, R and r,

    d) the efficiency η in terms of ϵ, R and r.

Example 1 – *Calculate the efficiency if a 20 Ω resistor is supplied from a 12 V battery with an internal resistance of 4 Ω.*

Total resistance is $20 + 4 = 24\ \Omega$, so current $I = \dfrac{12\ \text{V}}{24\ \Omega} = 0.50$ A.

Power in load $P = IV = I \times IR = I^2R = 0.50^2 \times 20 = 5.0$ W.

Power supplied $I\epsilon = 0.50 \times 12 = 6.0$ W. Efficiency $= \dfrac{5.0\ \text{W}}{6.0\ \text{W}} = 0.83$

10.2   Calculate the load power P for an $\epsilon = 240$ V generator with internal resistance 2.5 Ω when it is supplying 4.2 A. Hint: use $\epsilon = V + Ir$

10.3   Calculate the efficiency η of the generator in question 10.2.

10.4 An $\epsilon = 12$ V battery has an internal resistance $r = 4.0\,\Omega$. Fill in the missing entries in the table below.

R / Ω	V / V	I / A	P / W	Efficiency η
0.10	(a)	(b)	(c)	(d)
2.0	(e)	(f)	(g)	(h)
4.0	(i)	(j)	(k)	(l)
6.0	(m)	(n)	(o)	(p)
50	(q)	(r)	(s)	(t)

10.5 Use your answers to question 10.4 to state the value of r/R which gives the greatest load power P for given, fixed values of ϵ and r.

10.6 Use your answers to question 10.4 (or other reasoning) to state the value of r/R which gives the greatest efficiency for given values of ϵ and r.

10.7 Calculate r if $P = 500$ MW, $V = 23$ kV and $\eta = 0.99$.

Example 2 – *The load resistor R in the circuit shown is replaced by $30\,\Omega$ and $60\,\Omega$ heaters wired in parallel. Calculate the power dissipated in the $30\,\Omega$ heater if $\epsilon = 230$ V and $r = 3.0\,\Omega$.*

Resistance of the two heaters in parallel $R = \left(30^{-1} + 60^{-1}\right)^{-1} = 20\,\Omega$.

Total circuit resistance $= 20 + 3 = 23\,\Omega$, so current $= \dfrac{230\text{ V}}{23\,\Omega} = 10$ A.

Voltage across the heaters is $V = IR = 10\text{ A} \times 20\,\Omega = 200$ V.

Power in $30\,\Omega$ heater is given by $\dfrac{\text{Voltage}^2}{\text{Resistance}} = \dfrac{200^2}{30} = 1300$ W to 2sf.

10.8 An $\epsilon = 5.4$ V power supply (with $r = 8.0\,\Omega$) powers a $50\,\Omega$ phone. A voltmeter (with resistance $200\,\Omega$) is connected to measure V.

   a) How much voltage V is measured across the phone?

   b) Calculate the power delivered to the phone.

10.9 Calculate the voltage, current and power for each of the resistors in the circuit below.

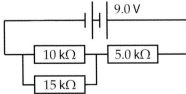

11 Path and phase difference

When waves of the same frequency arrive at a position from more than one source or route, it is helpful to calculate how they will interfere. The path and phase difference tell us whether they will interfere constructively or destructively.

Example context: a microphone placed between two speakers can receive either a strong or weak signal depending on where it is placed.

Quantities: λ wavelength (m) f frequency (Hz)
                     v wave speed $(\mathrm{m\,s^{-1}})$ ΔL path difference (m)
                     D distance to screen (m) $\Delta\phi$ phase difference $(°)$
                     d slit separation (m) N slits per mm $(\mathrm{mm^{-1}})$
                     θ angle from axis $(°)$ y distance from axis (m)
                     n order of interference (no unit) $n = 0, 1, 2, 3...$ if constructive

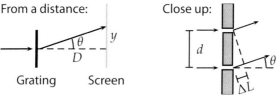

From a distance: Close up:

Grating   Screen

Equations: $v = f\lambda$ $\Delta\phi = \dfrac{\Delta L}{\lambda} \times 360°$ $y = D\tan\theta$ $d = \dfrac{1\,\mathrm{mm}}{N}$
              For slits: $\Delta L = d\sin\theta$ Small angles: $\tan\theta \approx \sin\theta$

11.1   Use the equations to derive expressions for

     a) the phase difference $\Delta\phi$ in terms of d, θ and λ,

     b) $\sin\theta$ for constructive interference in terms of λ, n and d,

     c) $\sin\theta$ for constructive interference in terms of λ, n and N,

     d) $\sin\theta$ for constructive interference in terms of n, N, f and v,

     e) y for $n = 1$ in terms of λ, D and d if θ is small,

     f) y for $n = 5$ in terms of f, v, D and d if θ is small,

     g) ΔL for a microphone placed between two speakers connected to the same signal. The speakers are a distance D apart, and the microphone is a distance y from the mid point.

11.2   Calculate $\Delta\phi$ (as an angle less than $360°$) for $\Delta L = 40.0$ cm if $\lambda = 3.6$ cm.

Example 1 – *Calculate $\Delta\phi$ between the two routes below. $\lambda = 12$ cm*

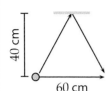

40 cm

60 cm

Longer route: $L = 2 \times \sqrt{30^2 + 40^2} = 100$ cm.
Direct route: $L = 60$ cm. $\Delta L = 100 - 60 = 40$ cm.
$$\Delta\phi = \frac{\Delta L}{\lambda} \times 360° = \frac{40}{12} \times 360° = \left(3\tfrac{1}{3}\right) \times 360°.$$
Ignoring the 3 whole rotations, which do not affect the interference, $\Delta\phi = \tfrac{1}{3} \times 360° = 120°$.

11.3   A 440 Hz sound wave reaches a microphone by two routes. The sound travels 2.50 m directly and travels 4.00 m if it reflects off a wall on the way. Calculate the phase difference on arrival. Assume that $v = 330$ m s^{-1}.

Example 2 – *Light from a sodium lamp passes a grating with 650 lines mm^{-1} and then strikes a wall which is $D = 50.0$ cm from the grating. The grating and wall are both at right angles to the original ray. The first order ($n = 1$) interference hits the wall $y = 20.7$ cm from the centre. Calculate the wavelength.*
$$d = \frac{1.0 \times 10^{-3} \text{ m}}{650} = 1.538 \times 10^{-6} \text{ m}; \theta = \tan^{-1}\left(\frac{0.207}{0.500}\right) = 22.49°$$
$n = 1$ so $\lambda = d \sin\theta = 1.538 \times 10^{-6}$ m $\times \sin(22.49°) = 5.88 \times 10^{-7}$ m.

11.4   A grating with 450 lines mm^{-1} is 75.0 cm from a wall. Light shines perpendicular to both grating and wall onto the centre of the grating.

    a) Calculate the angle θ for the $n = 1$ diffraction of 450 nm blue light.

    b) Calculate the $n = 1$ distance y for 633 nm light.

    c) Calculate λ for $n = 1$ light with $y = 27.8$ cm.

    d) Visible light has wavelengths in the range 400 nm $< \lambda < 700$ nm. How wide is the colourful $n = 1$ pattern on the wall?

11.5   20 GHz microwaves pass through a pair of narrow slits 10 cm apart. Calculate the fringe spacing (y when $n = 1$) on a screen 2.00 m behind the slits.

11.6   Calculate the smallest angle θ at which you would get destructive ($\Delta\phi = 180°$) interference when 550 nm light passes two slits 50 μm apart.

11.7   Using $v = 330$ m s^{-1}, calculate $\Delta\phi$ for a microphone placed between two speakers which are 1.5 m apart if

    a) $f = 440$ Hz and the microphone is 37.5 cm from one speaker,

    b) $f = 660$ Hz and the microphone is 65 cm from one speaker.

11.8   Two synchronised 10 GHz microwave transmitters face each other. How far from the mid point is the first place with $\Delta\phi = 60°$?

12 Diffraction, interference and multiple slits

It is helpful to be able to determine the the path difference and phase difference of rays that originate from non-adjacent multiple slits.

Example context: multiple slits in a diffraction grating enable the interference fringes to be brighter and narrower. This is useful in spectroscopy.

Quantities: L path length (m) λ wavelength (m)
ΔL path difference (m) $\Delta\phi$ phase difference (°)
d slit separation (m) D distance to screen (m)
Subscripts $_{1,2,3,4}$ label different paths.

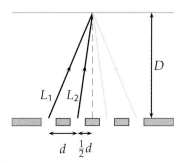

$$d \quad \tfrac{1}{2}d$$

Equations: $\Delta\phi = \dfrac{\Delta L}{\lambda} \times 360°$ $c^2 = a^2 + b^2$ (Pythagoras)

12.1 Use the equations and the diagram to derive expressions for

a) the path lengths L_1 and L_2 in terms of d and D,

b) the largest λ for destructive interference in terms of L_1 and L_2,

c) the largest λ for destructive interference in terms of d and D.

12.2 In the diagram above, $d = 1.00$ mm and $D = 4.00$ m. Calculate the largest wavelength that produces total destructive interference in the centre of the screen.

Example – *Calculate the phase difference between the first and third slit at the point opposite the first slit, when $d = 1.00$ mm, $D = 2.00$ m and $\lambda = 700$ nm.*

$$\frac{L_3 - L_1}{\lambda} = \frac{\sqrt{2.00^2 + (2.00 \times 10^{-3})^2} - 2.00}{700 \times 10^{-9}}$$

$= 1.429$, so $\Delta\phi = 360° \times 1.429 = 514°$.

Subtracting the whole cycle gives $154°$.

12.3 In the diagram here, $D = 5.00$ m, $d = 1.00$ mm and $\lambda = 600$ nm. For the spot directly opposite slit 1, calculate

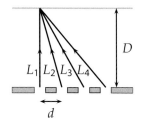

    a) the ΔL between L_2 and L_3,

    b) the $\Delta\phi$ between L_2 and L_3,

    c) the ΔL between L_1 and L_4,

    d) the $\Delta\phi$ between L_1 and L_4.

12.4 Describe the appearance of the spot opposite slit 1 in question 12.3.

12.5 In the diagram here, $D = 2.50$ m, $d = 1.00$ mm and $\lambda = 400$ nm. For the spot directly opposite the point half-way between slit 1 and 2, calculate

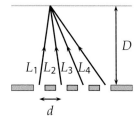

    a) the ΔL between L_1 and L_3,

    b) the $\Delta\phi$ between L_1 and L_3,

    c) the ΔL between L_2 and L_4,

    d) the $\Delta\phi$ between L_2 and L_4.

12.6 Describe the appearance of the spot directly opposite the point half-way between slit 1 and 2 in question 12.5.

12.7 The screen in question 12.6 is moved to a distance of 5.00 m from the slits, by the rest of the experimental setup remains the same. Calculate

    a) the ΔL between L_1 and L_3,   c) the ΔL between L_2 and L_4,

    b) the $\Delta\phi$ between L_1 and L_3,   d) the $\Delta\phi$ between L_2 and L_4.

12.8 Describe the appearance of the spot directly opposite the point half-way between slit 1 and 2 in question 12.7.

12.9 A single slit can be thought of as six individual slits. In the diagram here, $D = 20.0$ cm, the width of the slit $d = 1.00$ mm and $\lambda = 600$ nm. For the spot directly opposite the individual slit 6, calculate

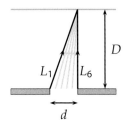

    a) the $\Delta\phi$ between L_1 and L_4,

    b) the $\Delta\phi$ between L_2 and L_5,

    c) the $\Delta\phi$ between L_3 and L_6,

    d) the appearance of the spot.

13 Reflection and refraction – angle of acceptance and prisms

It is helpful to be able to calculate the angle of acceptance for light entering an optical fibre; that is, the maximum angle of incidence that causes total internal reflection within the fibre. As a starting point, consider a prism.

Example context: A beam of light from a laser is directed towards a glass triangular prism. At large enough angles of incidence, the light passes through the prism. At small enough angles of incidence, the light undergoes total internal reflection within the prism.

Quantities: θ_1 incidence angle (°) θ_2 refraction angle (°)
                       θ_3 incidence angle (°) θ_4 refraction angle (°)
                       n_A refractive index of air n_G refractive index of glass
                       α prism angle (°)

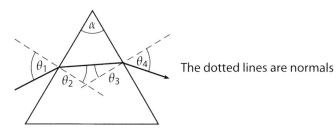

The dotted lines are normals

Equations: $n_A \sin \theta_1 = n_G \sin \theta_2$ $n_G \sin \theta_3 = n_A \sin \theta_4$ $\alpha = \theta_2 + \theta_3$

13.1   Use the diagram above and the equations to derive expressions for
         a) the refracted angle θ_2 in terms of θ_1 and the refractive indices,
         b) the incidence angle θ_3 in terms of α, θ_1 and the refractive indices,
         c) the refraction angle θ_4 in terms of α, θ_1 and the refractive indices.

13.2   Fill in the missing entries in the table below.

n_G	n_A	$\alpha/°$	$\theta_1/°$	$\theta_2/°$	$\theta_3/°$	$\theta_4/°$
1.52	1.00	40.0	40.0	(a)	(b)	(c)
1.38	1.00	65.0	35.0	(d)	(e)	(f)
1.50	1.00	60.0	28.0	(g)	(h)	(i)

Example – *Calculate the outgoing refraction angle θ_4 for a prism ($\alpha = 60.0°$) made of glass ($n_G = 1.50$) in air ($n_A = 1.00$) when the incoming incidence angle $\theta_1 = 40°$.*

$$\theta_2 = \sin^{-1}\left(\frac{n_A}{n_G}\sin\theta_1\right) = \sin^{-1}\left(\frac{1.00}{1.50}\times\sin 40°\right) = 25.37°$$

$$\theta_3 = \alpha - \theta_2 = 60.0° - 25.37° = 34.63°$$

$$\theta_4 = \sin^{-1}\left(\frac{n_G}{n_A}\sin\theta_3\right) = \sin^{-1}\left(\frac{1.50}{1.00}\times\sin 34.63°\right) = 58.5°$$

13.3 Total internal reflection occurs when the incidence angle is greater than the critical angle. The critical angle is the incidence angle that would produce a refraction angle of $90.0°$. Calculate the critical angle for the glass-air boundary when $n_G = 1.50$.

13.4 For a $60.0°$ prism made of the same glass as question 13.3, calculate the minimum incidence angle θ_1 that does not produce total internal reflection within the prism. *(Hint, let $\theta_4 = 90.0°$)*

Optical fibres are similar to prisms, except instead of air, the glass core is clad with a slightly different glass. The same equations as were used so far can be used for optical fibres, where n_A becomes the cladding refractive index and n_G becomes the core refractive index.

13.5 Calculate the critical angle for core-cladding optical fibre boundary when $n_G = 1.51$ and $n_A = 1.49$.

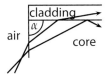

13.6 An optical fibre can be thought of like a $90°$ prism, except θ_1 is in air and θ_4 is in the cladding. If the core and cladding have the same refractive indices as question 13.5, calculate the maximum incidence angle θ_1 that can produce total internal reflection within the fibre. (This is called the angle of acceptance)

13.7 An optical fibre has a core with refractive index 1.55 and cladding with refractive index 1.49. Calculate the angle of acceptance.

14 Optical path

It is helpful to be able to calculate the optical path length for a ray of light passing through a medium. This enables us to study interference in different media.

Example context: a beam of light passes through a beam splitter that causes 50% of the intensity to travel along a path in the air, and the other 50% of the intensity to pass through the same distance path through water. When the two beams are brought back together, they interfere.

Quantities: n refractive index ℓ optical path length (m)
                  x geometric path length (m) $\Delta\phi$ phase difference (°)
                  $\Delta\ell$ optical path difference (m) λ wavelength in air (m)
                  Subscripts $_{1,2}$ label different paths

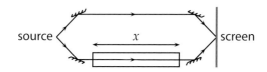

Equations: $\Delta\phi = \dfrac{\Delta\ell}{\lambda} \times 360°$ $\ell = n\,x$ $\Delta\ell = \ell - x$

14.1   Use the equations and the diagram above to derive expressions for

        a) the phase difference $\Delta\phi$ in terms of ℓ, x and λ,

        b) the phase difference $\Delta\phi$ in terms of n, x and λ,

        c) the shortest geometric path length x through a medium of refractive index n that causes destructive interference.

Example 1 – *Using the diagram above, calculate the shortest geometric path length through water ($n = 1.35$) that causes red light ($\lambda = 700$ nm) to destructively interfere.*

$\Delta\ell = \frac{1}{2}\lambda$ so $nx - x = \frac{1}{2}\lambda$ and $x = \dfrac{\lambda}{2\,(n-1)} = \dfrac{700 \times 10^{-9}}{2\,(1.35 - 1)} = 1.00\ \mu m$

14.2   Using the diagram above, calculate the shortest geometric path length through glass ($n = 1.50$) that causes purple light ($\lambda = 400$ nm) to destructively interfere.

14.3 Using the diagram on page 27, complete the table below.

$\Delta\phi$ / °	λ / nm	n	x / μm
(a)	700	1.35	1.00
360	(b)	1.40	1.50
270	550	(c)	0.500
90.0	630	2.20	(d)

Example 2 – *Normal rays reflect off the two sides of a sheet of glass ($n = 1.50$), thickness $d = 1.20$ μm. The rays have a wavelength $\lambda = 654$ nm. Ray 1 (see diagram) has a phase change of $180°$ on reflection, Ray 2 does not. Calculate the phase difference between the reflected rays 1 and 2 outside the glass.*

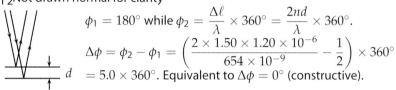

1 2Not drawn normal for clarity

$$\phi_1 = 180° \text{ while } \phi_2 = \frac{\Delta\ell}{\lambda} \times 360° = \frac{2nd}{\lambda} \times 360°.$$

$$\Delta\phi = \phi_2 - \phi_1 = \left(\frac{2 \times 1.50 \times 1.20 \times 10^{-6}}{654 \times 10^{-9}} - \frac{1}{2}\right) \times 360°$$

d $= 5.0 \times 360°$. Equivalent to $\Delta\phi = 0°$ (constructive).

14.4 A thin film of soapy water ($n = 1.25$) is illuminated with coherent mono-chromatic yellow light ($\lambda = 580$ nm) normal to the surface. Calculate the minimum thickness of soapy water film for destructive interference.

14.5 A thin film of soapy water ($n = 1.25$) is illuminated with coherent blue light ($\lambda_1 = 450$ nm) and coherent orange light ($\lambda_2 = 600$ nm) normal to the surface. Calculate the minimum thickness of soapy water film that causes destructive interference of

    a) blue light,   c) both blue and orange light.
    b) orange light,

14.6 A sheet of glass ($n = 1.50$) is slightly thicker at one side (see diagram). It is illuminated from above with coherent monochromatic red light ($\lambda = 700$ nm) normal to the surface. Calculate the number of dark fringes that would be observed from above the wedge.

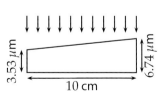

3.53 μm 10 cm   6.74 μm

16 Inverse square intensity

It is helpful to be able to calculate the intensity of a wave at different distances as it spreads out from a source.

Example context: the distance to a star can be calculated from a knowledge of its luminosity (power) and its brightness when seen from Earth. We can also work out the exposure to ionising radiation at different distances from a source.

Quantities: P Power (W) A Surface area (m^2)
                     I Intensity $(W\,m^{-2})$ r Distance from source (m)
                     C Count rate $(Bq = s^{-1})$
                     Subscripts label different locations, so I_1 is measured at r_1.

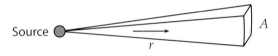

Equations: $A_{sphere} = 4\pi r^2$ $I = \dfrac{P}{A}$

16.1   For a source which radiates in all directions, use the equations to derive expressions for

         a)   the intensity I at a distance r from a source of power P,

         b)   The distance d at which a source P has intensity I.

         c)   the intensity I_2 at a distance r_2 from a source if the intensity at distance r_1 is I_1.

Example 1 – *The desk in a room is 1.7 m directly below a perfectly efficient light bulb. To read a 0.0625 m^2 (A4) sheet of paper comfortably, at least 27 mW of light must hit it. Calculate the minimum power of light bulb required.*

Intensity required $I = \dfrac{27 \times 10^{-3}\ W}{0.0625\ m^2} = 0.432\ W\,m^{-2}$.

If light spreads out 1.7 m in all directions, it will illuminate a spherical shape of area $A_{sphere} = 4\pi \times (1.7\ m)^2 = 36.3\ m^2$.

The power needed is $P = I A_{sphere} = 0.432 \times 36.3 = 16$ W.

16.2   Calculate the intensity if 130 W of light from a spotlight hits a 4.0 m $\times$ 3.0 m region of a stage.

16.3   The rear light on a bicycle gives off 0.15 W of light in all backwards directions. Calculate the intensity of light 23 m behind the lamp.

16.4 Someone can see a lamp providing the intensity is larger than $2.5 \times 10^{-7}\,\mathrm{W\,m^{-2}}$. How far away could this person see a 500 W warning lamp which gives off light in all directions?

16.5 When sunlight shines perpendicularly on a $0.6\,\mathrm{m} \times 1.2\,\mathrm{m}$ solar panel, 195 W of electricity is generated. This is 20% of the total radiation incident on it.

    a) Calculate the intensity of the sunlight at the panel.

    b) The Earth is 1.50×10^{11} m from the Sun. Calculate the Sun's power.

    c) How close to your eye would you need to hold a 150 W light bulb for it to appear as bright as the Sun? Assume that the Sun and the light bulb make visible light with the same efficiency.

Example 2 – *A gamma source is* 12.3 *cm from a detector, which records* 942 *background-corrected counts in* 30.0 *s. How many counts would you expect from the same detector in* 40.0 *s at a distance of* 16.8 *cm?*

The count rate C (in Bq) will be proportional to I at each distance.

Count rate at 12.3 cm $= \dfrac{942}{30} = 31.4$ Bq. Cr^2 is the same at all distances (it is proportional to P), so $31.4\,\mathrm{Bq} \times (12.3\,\mathrm{cm})^2 = C \times (16.8\,\mathrm{cm})^2$

$C = \dfrac{31.4 \times 12.3^2}{16.8^2} = 16.8$ Bq. Counts expected in 40 s $= 16.8 \times 40 = 673$.

16.6 When dentists take X-rays, they stand by the door, or outside the room. Calculate the intensity at 3.5 m from the source as a fraction of the intensity 0.32 m from it.

16.7 The background count in a laboratory is 36 counts in 40 s. When a gamma source is placed 1.5 m from the detector, there are 236 counts each minute.

    a) Calculate the background-corrected count rate in Bq.

    b) Calculate the expected background-corrected count rate 15 cm from the source.

16.8 On a very dark night, an astronomer can see a 5.3×10^{28} W star with their unaided eye providing the intensity is larger than $1.8 \times 10^{-10}\,\mathrm{W\,m^{-2}}$.

    a) How far away would the star be if it is only just visible?

    b) What is the minimum visible intensity with a telescope of diameter 7.5 cm rather than an eye with a pupil diameter of 0.75 cm.

    c) Another star of the same power is just visible using the telescope. How far away is it?

17 Banked tracks for turning

For an object travelling in a circular path, there must be a force pushing it inwards towards the centre of the circle. On a sloped (banked) track, the force from the inwards push of the bank (plus any friction) can provide this centripetal force.

Example context: A car travels along a smooth sloping (banked) track at constant speed and height. For a track of radius r, at the right speed and angle of slope the resultant force is the centripetal force needed.

We draw two diagrams: the forces on the car, and a vector diagram of the forces in which the resultant force is required to be horizontal. We can resolve (a) in directions H and V (so $mg = N\cos\theta$), or (b) $\parallel$ and $\perp$ to the slope (then $N = mg\cos\theta$). These are not both correct; this is not in equilibrium - the force diagram requires a horizontal resultant; so (a) (H and V) is the correct choice.

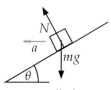

$$\text{required resultant force} = \frac{mv^2}{r}$$

Quantities:
m mass (kg)
r radius of path (m)
ω angular velocity (rad s^{-1})
t_p period of orbit (s)
N Normal contact force on car from track (N)

a acceleration inwards (m s^{-2})
v speed (m s^{-1})
θ angle of track $(°)$

Equations: $\quad F = ma \quad a_{\text{centripetal}} = \dfrac{v^2}{r} \quad v = r\omega \quad t_p = \dfrac{2\pi r}{v}$

17.1 A car of weight mg travels at constant speed v around a smooth, banked track of radius r and slope θ above the horizontal, and remains at a constant height up the slope. Use diagrams to write down expressions for

    a) N in terms of m, g and θ,

    b) v in terms of g, r and θ,

    c) t_p in terms of r, g and θ,

    d) N in terms of m, g, r and v,

    e) a in terms of v and ω,

    f) ω in terms of g, r and θ.

17.2 A motorbike of mass 160 kg moves in a circular path of radius 120 m at a speed of $15\,\text{m s}^{-1}$.

a) What is the resultant centripetal force on the motorbike?

b) Calculate the centripetal force as a fraction of the weight of the bike.

c) If the motor bike is driven along the slope of a smooth, banked circular track, what is the angle of the track to the horizontal that would provide this centripetal force?

17.3 A fairground experience consists of lying on a flat surface in a freely pivoted carriage being swung in a circle of radius 12 m. If the maximum force they can cope with is $6mg$, what is the minimum period of rotation t_p?

Example – *A smooth banked track is constructed around a flat circular service area of diameter 150 m. The width of the track surface is 30 m and the slope is at 15° to the horizontal. What is the highest constant speed that a motorbike can travel around the track so that it does not drive over the top of the bank?*

Radius of track at bank top $= 75 + (30 \cos 15°) = 104$ m

Now, $v^2 = rg \tan \theta = 104 \times 9.81 \times \tan 15°$

So, $v = 17\,\mathrm{m\,s^{-1}}$ to 2sf.

17.4 A small car travels around a rough circular track of radius 44 m, banked at 20° to the horizontal. The magnitude of the frictional force on the car pointing down the slope is equal to the weight of the car. At what speed v is the car travelling?

17.5 Car **A** travels at a speed of $20\,\mathrm{m\,s^{-1}}$ around a smooth banked circular track at an angle of 20° to the horizontal. It overtakes car **B** on the same track, also travelling in a circle of constant radius but at a speed of $22\,\mathrm{m\,s^{-1}}$. What is the minimum separation of the car centres when they pass?

17.6 A spherically shaped bowl of inner radius 16 cm is 8.0 cm deep at its centre, and contains a small marble. The bowl is rotated about a vertical axis. At what angular velocity ω will the marble leave the bowl?

17.7 A particle of mass m slides round in a circle of radius r on the inside of a smooth conical surface at a constant vertical height h above the apex, which is of angle 2α. What is the speed of the particle in terms of r, g and α?

17.8 A particle of mass $m = 0.40$ kg slides round the inside of a smooth conical surface (with the apex below) in a horizontal circle of radius $r = 20$ cm at speed $v = 3.2\,\mathrm{m\,s^{-1}}$. The angle of the apex is $2\alpha = 30°$ and the particle is attached to the apex by a light wire, which prevents it rising up the conical surface. What is the tension T in the wire?

17.9 The standard railway gauge has tracks separated by 1435 mm on banked sleepers. Calculate the vertical displacement between the two tracks such that a train travelling at $180\,\mathrm{km\,h^{-1}}$ along a curve of radius 1500 m will experience a normal reaction force on the wheels only.

18   Conical pendulum

A particle of mass m at the end of a light string fixed to a point can be set in motion so that it moves in a horizontal circle centred below the point of suspension.

Example context: Fairground rides, mechanical speed controllers; examples are closely related to those on smooth banked tracks, as the normal reaction force of the track is replaced by tension in a string or rod. In the diagram, the tension in the string and the weight are not aligned, so the object is not in equilibrium. A resultant force of constant magnitude is directed horizontally towards the centre of the circle, so the forces should be resolved horizontally and vertically.

(the view from above)

$$s = r\theta \qquad \frac{s}{t} = r\frac{\theta}{t} = r\omega$$

Quantities:	T tension in the string (N)	a acceleration inwards $(\mathrm{m\,s^{-2}})$
	r radius of orbit (m)	ω angular velocity $(\mathrm{rad\,s^{-1}})$
	ϕ angle to vertical $(°)$	f frequency $(\mathrm{s^{-1}, Hz})$
	ℓ length of string (m)	t_p period (s)
	v speed of object $(\mathrm{m\,s^{-1}})$	θ angle of rotation $(\mathrm{rad\,s^{-1}})$

Equations: $\qquad F = ma \quad a_\text{centripetal} = r\omega^2 \quad v = r\omega \quad \omega = 2\pi f \quad t_\mathrm{p} = \dfrac{1}{f}$

18.1   A metal ball of mass m is attached to a light string of length ℓ and moves in a horizontal circular path at an angular velocity ω. Use diagrams to write down expressions for

a) the angular velocity ω of the ball in terms of ϕ, r and g,

b) the period of orbit, t_p, in terms of ϕ, r and g,

c) the [horizontal] acceleration of the ball, a in terms of ϕ and g,

d) the acceleration of the ball, a, in terms of m, T and ϕ,

e) the tension in the string, T, in terms of m, g, r and ω,

f) $\cos\phi$ in terms of ℓ and r,

g) the angular velocity ω in terms of g, ℓ and r,

h) $\cos\phi$ in terms of g, r and ω,

i) v in terms of ϕ, r and g,

j) t_p in terms of v and a.

Example – *A small ball of mass* 0.60 *kg is suspended at the end of a light string of length* 0.80 *m attached to the ceiling. The ball travels in a horizontal circle about a vertical axis* 1.3 *times per second. How far below the ceiling is the ball?*
Resolving the forces on the sphere H and V, we obtain the two equations

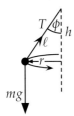

$$T \sin \phi = mr\omega^2 \quad \text{and} \quad T \cos \phi = mg$$

Dividing, $\quad \tan \phi = \dfrac{r\omega^2}{g} = \dfrac{r}{g} 4\pi^2 f^2$

But also, $\quad \tan \phi = \dfrac{r}{h} = \dfrac{r}{g} 4\pi^2 f^2$

Hence, $\quad h = \dfrac{9.81}{4\pi^2 \times 1.3^2} = 0.15$ m

18.2 A small sphere of mass 2.0 kg, attached to the end of a light string of length 90 cm at 24° to the vertical, moves in a horizontal circle. Calculate

    a) the tension T in the string, and

    b) the height h by which the mass is raised above its position at rest.

18.3 A lead ball of mass 45 g is attached to the end of an 80 cm long light string and swung around in a horizontal circle at high speed. If the string snaps at a tension of 195 N, what is the maximum frequency of rotation f possible?

18.4 A fairground ride consists of several small carriages (**c**) each supported at its centre of mass by a light cable of length $\ell = 2.20$ m with its upper end attached to a supporting ring of radius $R = 3.40$ m from the axis of rotation. What is the period when the carriages are rotating so that the cables are inclined at $\phi = 30.0°$ to the vertical?

18.5 A mechanical governor consists of a narrow central axle to which are hinged to two light rods of length ℓ, each attached to the centres of spherical masses of radius r. At what angular velocity ω, in terms of g, ℓ and r, will the spheres lose contact with the axle?

18.6 A conical pendulum on Earth produces a period of 0.34 s for a 30° semi-angle of the cone. When the same pendulum is used on the Moon where $g = 1.6$ m s^{-2}, what would be the period for double the semi-angle?

18.7 An aircraft travelling at 160 knots maintains its altitude during a circular banked "rate one turn", which is a $3.0°$ s^{-1} turning rate. At what angle to the horizontal are the wings of the plane?   (1 knot $= 0.514$ m s^{-1})

19 Vertical circles

It is helpful to calculate the forces on an object travelling in a vertical circle.

Example context: we can calculate the speed you would have to drive over a hump-back bridge in order to leave the ground. We can also calculate the minimum speed a roller coaster car requires in order to loop-the-loop.

Quantities: u speed at bottom $(m\,s^{-1})$ m mass (kg)
v speed at top $(m\,s^{-1})$ N normal reaction (N) + means ↑
W weight (N) a centripetal acceleration $(m\,s^{-2})$
r radius of circle (m) F resultant force (N)

Equations: $F = ma$ $W = mg$ $a_{top} = \dfrac{v^2}{r}$ $a_{bottom} = \dfrac{u^2}{r}$

Gain in E_{GP} = Loss in E_K, so $mg \times 2r = \frac{1}{2}mu^2 - \frac{1}{2}mv^2$

19.1   For a roller coaster car travelling in a vertical circle on frictionless track (where upwards N are positive) write equations for

   a) N for the car at the bottom using W, m and a,

   b) N for the car at the bottom using m, r, g and u,

   c) N for the car at the top using W, m and a,

   d) N for the car at the top using m, r, g and v,

   e) N for the car at the top using m, r, g and u,

   f) the speed v needed at the top if $N = 0$,

   g) the speed u needed at the bottom if $N = 0$ at the top.

Example – *Calculate the normal reaction when a 1200 kg car is half way over a hump back bridge if it is travelling at 13 m s^{-1}. The radius of the bridge's arc is 23 m.*

Acceleration is downwards, so $W - N = ma$.

$$N = W - ma = mg - \frac{mv^2}{r} = m\left(g - \frac{v^2}{r}\right)$$

$$N = 1200 \times \left(9.81 - \frac{13^2}{23}\right) = 3000 \text{ N to 2sf.}$$

19.2   Calculate the normal reaction for the car in the Example at a speed of 8.0 m s^{-1}.

19.3 For the car in the Example, calculate the speed at which the wheels would just leave the ground at the top of the bridge.

19.4 A 850 kg roller-coaster train goes over the top of a loop at $9.5 \mathrm{~m\,s^{-1}}$. The loop has a radius of 4.5 m. Calculate the reaction force on the train. Use a negative number if the force is downwards.

19.5 Fill in the missing entries in the table below for a 70 kg person riding a loop-the-loop roller-coaster. Give N and a as negative if they point downwards.

Top or Bottom	r / m	Speed / $\mathrm{m\,s^{-1}}$	a / $\mathrm{m\,s^{-2}}$	N / N
Top	7.5	6.0	(a)	(b)
Bottom	7.5	6.0	(c)	(d)
Top	7.5	12.0	(e)	(f)
Bottom	(g)	15	30	(h)

19.6 A person feels weightless when $N = 0$. Calculate the speed a roller-coaster car would have to be travelling at the top of an $r = 4.5$ m loop in order for the riders to experience weightlessness at the top.

19.7 An 850 g radio-controlled car is driven in circles around the inside of a large (empty) pipe with a radius of 90 cm. It travels at a steady $4.0 \mathrm{~m\,s^{-1}}$.

   a) Is the car going quickly enough not to fall off the pipe's surface?

   b) Calculate the normal reaction as the car passes the top.

   c) Calculate the normal reaction as the car passes the bottom.

19.8 When roller-coaster riders describe their rides, they call the ratio N/mg the g-force (this is not a scientific term). In this formula, N is taken as positive if it is directed upwards through the rider's body towards their head. A roller-coaster is designed to give $N/mg = 2.5$ at both the top and the bottom of the ride. The loop is not circular. The rider sits in a train which runs around the inside of the loop. The top of the loop is curved with a 7.6 m radius.

   a) State the value of N/mg for a rider sitting in the train at rest.

   b) Calculate the speed of the train at the top of the loop.

   c) If there is no friction, and the top of the loop is 21 m above the bottom, how fast will the train travel at the bottom of the loop?

   d) Calculate the radius of the loop at the bottom of the track.

20 Simple pendulum

A simple pendulum has a mass (called a bob) on the end of a light string which, when displaced from the vertical, swings back and forth with a time period which varies only with the length of the string and the acceleration due to gravity.

Example context: Simple pendulums can be found all around us, for example a swing on a playground or the timing mechanism inside a clock. If we can neglect air resistance then a simple pendulum will continue back and forth with the same amplitude and with a consistent time period. It is for these reasons that pendulums have been used to keep accurate time in clocks since 1656.

Quantities: θ angular displacement (rad)

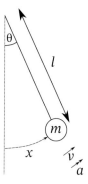

ω angular frequency (rad s^{-1})
f frequency (s^{-1})
x displacement (m)
v velocity (m s^{-1})
T period (s)
a linear acceleration (m s^{-2})
m mass (kg)
l length (m)
g acceleration due to gravity (m s^{-2})

Equations: $T = \dfrac{2\pi}{\omega}$ $\omega = \sqrt{\dfrac{g}{l}}$ $a = -\omega^2 x$ $f = \dfrac{1}{T}$ $\omega = 2\pi f$

$\sin\theta \approx \theta$ for small θ if θ is in radians

20.1   Use the pendulum diagram provided to

a) Write down an expression for the arc length (distance) x of the mass m from the vertical in terms of l and θ in radians.

b) Calculate the distance the bob travels if it moves through an angle of $60°$ and the pendulum string has a length of 30 cm.

c) Write down the **magnitude** of the resultant force that acts perpendicular to the string on mass m.

d) Use your result from part (c) with Newton's Second Law derive an expression for the linear acceleration, a of the bob in terms of g and θ, taking care with the direction of the resultant force perpendicular to the string and the direction of positive acceleration shown on the diagram.

e) Use the small angle approximation for $\sin\theta$ to simplify your expression for a found in part (d).

f) By combining your result from part (e) with your answer for question (a) rewrite the linear acceleration a in terms of g, l and x.

g) Finally compare your answer from part (f) with the Simple Harmonic Motion equation for acceleration in terms of displacement, $a = -\omega^2 x$ to show that $\omega^2 = g/l$.

Example – *A clock maker wishes to make a clock such that it ticks once every 2.0 s rather than every second. How long will the length of their pendulum need to be?*

$$T = 2\pi\sqrt{\frac{l}{g}} \quad \text{therefore} \quad l = g\left(\frac{T}{2\pi}\right)^2 = 9.81\left(\frac{2}{2\pi}\right)^2 \approx 1.0\,\text{m}$$

20.2   An astronaut takes a pendulum on a mission to Mars to estimate their weight on the planet. Their pendulum bob has a mass of 50 g, the length of the string is 0.5 m and the astronaut has a mass of 70 kg. The astronaut measures the period of the pendulum to be 2.3 s on Mars. How heavy is the astronaut on Mars to the nearest newton?

20.3   A simple pendulum is made of a light string of length $l = 25$ cm with a bob of mass $m = 30$ g and is stationed on the Moon ($g_m = 1.63\,\text{m s}^{-2}$)

a) What is the time period t_p for this pendulum?

b) How many whole oscillations does the pendulum make in 1 min

c) Calculate the angular frequency of this pendulum using l and g and show that it is numerically equal to $2\pi f$.

d) What would the value of t_p and ω be if we doubled the mass of the bob to $2m$?

20.4   In a lecture demonstration three pendulums are set in motion. The first has a length l, the second has a length $4l$ and the third has a length $9l$. If they all begin at the same amplitude and at the same time, how many whole swings will the first pendulum have completed after the initial drop when all three pendulums are instantaneously back in sync?

21 Electromagnetic induction – moving wire

When a wire moves through a perpendicular magnetic field, cutting through the magnetic flux lines, a voltage appears across it.

Example context: We can calculate the voltage induced in any moving conductor, even if it is not a complete loop.

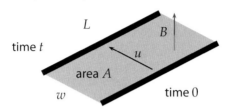

Quantities: B magnetic flux density (T)
w distance moved by wire (m)
L wire length (m)
A area swept through (m^2)
F_B magnetic force (N)
E electric field $(N C^{-1})$

u speed of wire $(m s^{-1})$
V induced voltage (V)
t time taken (s)
q charge of carriers (C)
F_E electric force (N)

Equations: $A = Lw$ $\quad w = ut$ $\quad V = \dfrac{d(BA)}{dt} = \dfrac{BA}{t}$
$F_B = quB$ $\quad F_E = qE$ $\quad E = V/L$

21.1 Use the equations to write down expressions for

a) the area A swept through by the wire using u, Δt and L,

b) the magnetic flux BA cut by the wire using u, Δt and L,

c) the rate of cutting flux $d(BA)/dt$,

d) the voltage V induced in the wire by Faraday's law,

e) the magnetic force on a charge q inside the wire,

f) the strength of an electric field E along the wire that could produce the same force on the charge,

g) the voltage V that would exist between the ends of the wire, if that electric field was uniform.

21.2 Find V if $B = 0.50$ T, $L = 0.050$ m and $u = 2.0$ m s^{-1}.

> **Example** – *At a certain point in the cycle of a generator, one 12 cm length of wire in the coil moves at 25 m s^{-1} perpendicular to its length and to a 0.70 T magnetic field. What voltage would be induced across this wire at that point?*
>
> $$V = \frac{BA}{t} = BLu = 0.70 \times 0.12 \times 25 = 2.1 \text{ V}$$

21.3 In a magnetic brake system on a roller-coaster, a metal bar of width 35 mm on the carriage moves through an electromagnet attached to the rails, where $B = 0.4$ T. If the carriage is moving at 70 m s^{-1} when it enters the brake, what is the initial voltage induced across the width of the bar?

21.4 In an experiment, a student induces a voltage of 15 mV by moving a 0.30 m-long section of wire through a region of uniform perpendicular magnetic field 0.35 T. At what speed were they moving the wire?

21.5 When 20 cm of straight wire is moved between the poles of a supercon-ducting magnet at 25 mm s^{-1}, a 35 mV voltage is induced. Find the mag-netic flux density between the poles.

21.6 Fill in the missing entries in the table below for a wire moving through a perpendicular magnetic field.

w / m	t / s	u / m s^{-1}	L / m	B / T	V / V
		6.0	0.50	1.2	(a)
		100	(b)	0.08	0.40
0.05	0.075	(c)	0.045	(d)	3.0×10^{-3}
1.35	(e)	15	1.5	5.0	(f)

21.7 In a motor, each long side of a turn in the coil acts like a 2.0 cm wire moving at 7.3 m s^{-1}. The strongest field it experiences during a cycle is 300 mT. If each turn has two long sides in series, what is the minimum number of turns in series needed to get a peak voltage greater than 3 V?

21.8 A metal aircraft with a 15.0 m wingspan is flying North at 450 km h^{-1}. What voltage could be induced between the wingtips, if the Earth's magnetic field has strength 60.0 μT and is pointing:

   a) vertically up from the Earth's surface?

   b) inclined at 20.0° from the vertical towards the horizontal South-North direction? [Hint: the flux lines will be spaced farther apart.]

22 Electromagnetic induction – rotating coil

It is helpful to be able to calculate the voltage, or electromotive force (EMF) induced by a rotating coil in a magnetic field.

Example context: most generators contain a coil of wire rotating uniformly in a uniform magnetic field. Whenever a there is a conductor in a changing magnetic field, an EMF is induced.

Quantities:
ε EMF (V) N number of turns
ϕ magnetic flux (Wb) B flux density (T)
A_0 coil area (m^2) t time (s)
A component of coil area linking flux (m^2)
ω angular frequency $(rad\ s^{-1})$
Subscript $_{rms}$ represents root mean square values
$\frac{d}{dt}$ means *rate of change of a quantity*

Equations:
$$\varepsilon = -N\frac{d\phi}{dt} \qquad \phi = BA \qquad A = A_0\cos\omega t$$

$$\varepsilon_{rms} = \sqrt{(\varepsilon^2)_{mean}} \qquad \frac{d\cos\omega t}{dt} = -\omega\sin\omega t$$

22.1 Use the equations to derive expressions for
    a) the magnetic flux ϕ in terms of B, A_0 and t,
    b) the EMF ε in terms of B, A_0, N, ω and t,
    c) the maximum EMF ε_{max},
    d) the root mean squared EMF ε_{rms} in terms of ε_{max}.

22.2 Fill in the missing entries in the table below.

ε_{max} / V	N	B / mT	A_0 / cm^2	ω / rad s^{-1}
(a)	100	50.0	5.00	31.4
2.50	(b)	80	10.0	157
1.70	50.0	(c)	12.5	62.8
325	25.0	100	(d)	314
325	1000	103	100	(e)

> **Example 1** – *A single circular loop of wire has a diameter of* 30.0 *cm and is rotated at* 1500 *rpm in a uniform magnetic field of flux density* 150 *mT. Calculate the maximum EMF induced.*
>
> $$\phi = BA = BA_0 \cos \omega t \text{ so } \varepsilon = -NBA_0 \tfrac{d}{dt} \cos \omega t = NBA_0 \omega \sin \omega t$$
>
> $$\varepsilon_{max} = NBA_0 \omega = 1 \times 0.150 \times \frac{\pi \times 0.300^2}{4} \times 1500 \frac{2\pi}{60} = 1.67 \text{ V}$$

22.3 A 5.00 cm long square coil with 10 turns is slowly rotated in a magnetic field of 80.0 mT at a rate of 20.0 rpm (revolutions per minute). Calculate

a) the angular frequency in rad s^{-1},

b) the magnitude of the EMF induced 1.00 s after the EMF was zero,

c) the magnitude of the maximum EMF induced.

22.4 A circular coil of diameter 10.0 cm with 50 turns is rotated in a magnetic field at 100 Hz. Calculate the flux density B that would induce a peak EMF of

a) 6.00 V,   b) 3.00 V,   c) 1.50 V.

22.5 A circular coil of radius 12.0 cm with 100 turns is rotated in a magnetic field of 500 mT. Calculate the angular frequency ω for a peak EMF of

a) 2.00 V,   b) 4.00 V,   c) 8.00 V.

> **Example 2** – *Calculate the magnetic flux density B necessary to generate* $V_{rms} = 230$ *V at* 50.0 *Hz with a square coil of length* 1.00 *m and* 50 *turns.*
>
> $$B = \frac{\sqrt{2}\varepsilon_{rms}}{NA_0\omega} = \frac{\sqrt{2} \times 230}{50 \times 1^2 \times (2\pi \times 50.0)} = 20.7 \text{ mT}$$

22.6 A circular coil with 1000 turns has a diameter of 5.00 cm and is rotating at 50.0 Hz in a uniform magnetic field of flux density 100 mT. Calculate

a) the magnitude of the EMF 2.50 ms after it was zero,

b) the magnitude of the EMF 5.00 ms after it was zero,

c) the time after the EMF was zero when the EMF reaches its maximum magnitude,

d) the root mean squared EMF.

22.7 Two identical coils rotate at identical rates. *Coil A* is in a uniform magnetic field strength that is double that of *coil B*. Calculate the ratio of the root mean square EMF of *coil A* compared to *coil B*.

23 Energy and fields – accelerator

It is helpful to be able to calculate the kinetic energy, momentum or speed of a charged particle which has been accelerated by a known voltage.

Example context: many particle accelerators, and the electron guns in older TVs and oscilloscopes, produce beams of charged particles using an electric field. A knowledge of the accelerating voltage enables the speed to be calculated.

Quantities: m mass (kg) q charge (C)
                        p momentum $(\mathrm{kg\,m\,s^{-1}})$ K kinetic energy (J)
                        u initial speed $(\mathrm{m\,s^{-1}})$ V accelerating voltage (V)
                        v final speed $(\mathrm{m\,s^{-1}})$ E electric field $(\mathrm{N\,C^{-1}})$
                        F force (N) L length of accelerating region (m)
                        λ wavelength (m)

Equations: $p = mv$ $\Delta K = K_{\text{final}} - K_{\text{initial}} = \tfrac{1}{2}mv^2 - \tfrac{1}{2}mu^2$ $\Delta K = qV$

$$\lambda = \frac{h}{p} \qquad F = qE \qquad \Delta K = FL \qquad 1\,\mathrm{eV} = 1.6 \times 10^{-19}\,\mathrm{J}$$

23.1   Use the equations to derive expressions for

        a) the momentum p in terms of V, m and q if $u = 0$,

        b) the speed v in terms of V, m and q if $u = 0$,

        c) the speed v if $u \neq 0$,

        d) the additional kinetic energy ΔK in terms of E, L and q,

        e) the electric field E in terms of V and L,

        f) the momentum p in terms of E, L, m and q if $u = 0$,

        g) the wavelength λ in terms of V, m and q when $u = 0$.

Example – *Calculate the voltage needed to accelerate an electron to $1.2 \times 10^7\,\mathrm{m\,s^{-1}}$ from rest.*

$$K = \tfrac{1}{2}mv^2 = \tfrac{1}{2} \times 9.11 \times 10^{-31} \times \left(1.2 \times 10^7\right)^2 = 6.552 \times 10^{-17}\,\mathrm{J}$$

$$V = \frac{K}{q} = \frac{6.552 \times 10^{-17}}{1.60 \times 10^{-19}} = 410\,\mathrm{V}$$

23.2   Calculate the voltage needed to accelerate a proton to $3.5 \times 10^6\,\mathrm{m\,s^{-1}}$ from rest.

23.3 Calculate the voltage needed to accelerate an electron to $3.5 \times 10^6 \, \text{m s}^{-1}$ from rest.

23.4 A 1.00 MeV proton has a kinetic energy of 1.0×10^6 eV.

    a) Express this energy in joules.

    b) Calculate the speed of the proton.

    c) What is the accelerating voltage needed to produce it?

    d) Calculate its momentum.

    e) Calculate its wavelength.

23.5 The electron gun in an old TV accelerates electrons from rest with 3.0 kV.

    a) Calculate the final speed of the electrons.

    b) Calculate the momentum of the electrons.

    c) Calculate the wavelength of the electrons.

23.6 Fill in the missing entries in the table below.

Particle	Energy / MeV	Momentum / kg m s^{-1}	Speed / m s^{-1}
Electron	0.001 50	(a)	(b)
Proton	10.0	(c)	(d)
Electron	(e)	4.55×10^{-24}	(f)
Proton	(g)	8.35×10^{-21}	(h)
Alpha particle	5.0	(i)	(j)

23.7 Calculate the final speed of a proton which was travelling at $2.5 \times 10^6 \, \text{m s}^{-1}$ before being accelerated through 1.4 MV.

23.8 Calculate the accelerating voltage required to accelerate particles from rest to achieve the desired wavelength.

    a) Electrons of wavelength 2.0 nm.

    b) Electrons of wavelength 20 nm.

    c) Protons of wavelength 1.5×10^{-13} m.

    d) Alpha particles of wavelength 1.5×10^{-14} m.

24 Energy and fields – relativistic accelerator

It is helpful to study particles which have been accelerated to a speed comparable to the speed of light c. The formulae of Special Relativity have to be used in place of $p = mv$ and $K = \frac{1}{2}mv^2$.

Example context: most particle accelerators produce beams of charged particles at speeds which are high enough to require Special Relativity.

Quantities: m rest mass (kg) q charge (C)
                  p momentum (kg m s^{-1}) K kinetic energy (J)
                  v speed (m s^{-1}) E total energy (J)
                  c speed of light (m s^{-1}) V accelerating voltage (V)
                  λ wavelength (m) γ relativistic factor (no unit)

Equations: $p = \gamma m v$ $E = \gamma m c^2$ $\lambda = \dfrac{h}{p}$ $\gamma = \left(1 - \dfrac{v^2}{c^2}\right)^{-\frac{1}{2}}$

                 $E = K + mc^2$ $K = qV$ $1 \text{ eV} = 1.6 \times 10^{-19} \text{ J}$

In these questions, all particles start from rest.

24.1   Use the equations to derive expressions for

       a) γ in terms of c, V, q and m,

       b) v in terms of c and γ,

       c) v in terms of c, V, q and m,

       d) p^2 in terms of E, m and c (without v or γ),

       e) p^2 in terms of c, V, q and m.

Example 1 – *Calculate the voltage needed to produce 2.5×10^8 m s^{-1} electrons.*

$$\gamma = \left(1 - \frac{v^2}{c^2}\right)^{-\frac{1}{2}} = \left(1 - \frac{2.5^2}{3^2}\right)^{-\frac{1}{2}} = 1.809$$

$$K = E - mc^2 = \gamma mc^2 - mc^2 = (\gamma - 1)\,mc^2$$

$$= 0.809 \times 9.11 \times 10^{-31} \times \left(3.00 \times 10^8\right)^2 = 6.633 \times 10^{-14} \text{ J}$$

$$V = K/q = 6.633 \times 10^{-14}/1.60 \times 10^{-19} = 415 \text{ kV}$$

24.2   Calculate the voltage needed to produce 2.7×10^8 m s^{-1} electrons.

24.3 Calculate the voltage needed to produce 2.7×10^8 m s^{-1} protons.

24.4 Calculate the voltage needed to produce 2.7×10^8 m s^{-1} alpha particles.

24.5 Calculate v/c for a particle with
  a) $E = mc^2$, c) $K = 2mc^2$,
  b) $E = 2mc^2$ d) $K = 7mc^2$.

24.6 Calculate the speed of a proton accelerated by 2.0 MV.

24.7 Calculate the speed of an electron accelerated by 2.0 MV.

Example 2 – *Calculate the momentum of a proton accelerated to a kinetic energy of* $1.0\,GeV = 10^9 \times 1.60 \times 10^{-19}\,J = 1.60 \times 10^{-10}\,J.$

$$E = K + mc^2 = 1.60 \times 10^{-10} + 1.67 \times 10^{-27} \times \left(3.00 \times 10^8\right)^2$$

$$= 3.103 \times 10^{-10}\,J$$

$$E^2 = p^2c^2 + m^2c^4 \text{ so } p = \sqrt{\frac{E^2 - m^2c^4}{c^2}} = \sqrt{\left(\frac{E}{c}\right)^2 - (mc)^2}$$

$$p = \sqrt{\left(\frac{3.103 \times 10^{-10}}{3.00 \times 10^8}\right)^2 - (1.67 \times 10^{-27} \times 3.00 \times 10^8)^2}$$

$$= 9.05 \times 10^{-19}\,\text{kg m s}^{-1}$$

24.8 Calculate the momentum of a $E = 4.5$ GeV proton.

24.9 Calculate the momentum of an electron accelerated by 20 MV.

24.10 A particle speeds out from a collision in a particle detector. A calorimeter measures its total energy as 1.527×10^{-10} J. Its curved path in a magnetic field gives its momentum as 5.060×10^{-19} kg m s^{-1}.
  a) Calculate the rest mass m of the particle in kilograms.
  b) Calculate the rest mass in units of the electron's rest mass.

24.11 An experiment requires electrons with a wavelength of 1.20×10^{-12} m.
  a) Calculate the momentum of the electron.
  b) Calculate the total energy E of the electron.
  c) Calculate the accelerating voltage V.

25 Energy and fields – closest approach

It is useful to work out how close a charged particle can get to an atomic nucleus from its speed, its kinetic energy or the temperature of the material.

Example context: In Geiger and Marsden's gold foil experiment, alpha particles were fired at gold nuclei. Depending on how close they came to the nucleus, they were deflected by different angles. In nuclear fusion, small nuclei will only fuse if they come close enough for the strong nuclear force to act.

Quantities:
V electric potential (V)
U energy (J)
v initial speed $(\mathrm{m\,s^{-1}})$
m mass (kg)

Q charge of nucleus (C)
q charge of projectile (C)
r minimum separation (m)
T absolute temperature (K)

Equations:
$$V = \frac{Q}{4\pi\epsilon_0 r} \quad U = qV \quad U = \frac{mv^2}{2} \quad U = \frac{3k_B T}{2}$$

25.1 Assume that the large nucleus is held stationary in the material by interatomic forces. Use the equations to derive expressions for

  a) the distance of closest approach r in terms of energy U,

  b) the distance of closest approach r given the initial speed v,

  c) the distance of closest approach r given the temperature T.

Example 1 – *Calculate the distance of closest approach of a 10 MeV alpha particle to a gold nucleus (with 79 protons) in a direct collision where the nucleus remains stationary.*
We work out the energy of the alpha particle, remembering that it has two protons $U = qV = 2 \times 1.6 \times 10^{-19} \times 1.0 \times 10^7 = 3.2 \times 10^{-12}$ J. Now we calculate the distance of closest approach
$$r = \frac{Qq}{4\pi\epsilon_0 U} = \frac{(2 \times 1.6 \times 10^{-19})(79 \times 1.6 \times 10^{-19})}{4\pi\epsilon_0 \times 3.2 \times 10^{-12}} = 1.14 \times 10^{-14}\,\text{m}$$

25.2 Calculate the distance of closest approach of a proton travelling at 2.0×10^6 m s^{-1} to a copper nucleus with 29 protons. Assume that the copper nucleus remains stationary.

25.3 Repeat question 25.2 for a proton with half the speed.

25.4 How much kinetic energy would a proton need to have to approach a gold nucleus (79 protons) and to come within 2 fm of it?

25.5   Fill in the missing entries in the table below for collisions with a stationary gold nucleus.

Projectile	Energy	Closest approach distance
Proton	3.0×10^{-12} J	(a)
Proton	(b)	7.2×10^{-15} m
Alpha particle	(c)	18 fm
Positron	50 keV	(d)

25.6   For collisions of an alpha particle with a gold nucleus held stationary, calculate

   a) the distance of closest approach for $v = 1.5 \times 10^6$ m s^{-1},

   b) the distance of closest approach for $v = 3.0 \times 10^6$ m s^{-1},

   c) the initial speed needed for $r = 7.0$ fm,

   d) the initial speed needed for $r = 3.5$ fm.

Example 2 – *What temperature would be needed in order for two deuterium $\left(^{2}_{1}\text{H}\right)$ nuclei of typical speeds to come within 1.0 fm of each other?*
We need to remember that half of the energy for the approach comes from each nucleus. The total kinetic energy will be $U = 2 \times \frac{3}{2}k_B T = 3k_B T$.

$$3k_B T = U = \frac{Qq}{4\pi\epsilon_0 r}, \text{ so } T = \frac{qQ}{4\pi\epsilon_0 r}\frac{1}{3k_B} = \frac{Qq}{12\pi\epsilon_0 k_B r}$$

$$T = \frac{\left(1.6 \times 10^{-19}\right)^2}{12\pi\epsilon_0 k_B \times 1.0 \times 10^{-15}} = 5.6 \times 10^9 \text{ K}$$

25.7   What is the distance of closest approach of two gold nuclei if they have kinetic energies typical of material at 1.4×10^7 K?

25.8   What would be the wavelength of a proton which could come within 3.0 fm of a uranium nucleus with 92 protons which was held stationary? Hint: you may wish to revise the link on page 5.

26 Orbits

An orbit is the path that an object follows in a gravitational or electromagnetic field. This includes the paths of the planets around the Sun.

Example context: The planets of the solar system orbit around the Sun due to the gravitational force of attraction between the planets and the Sun. To accelerate a particle in orbit in a particle accelerator the magnetic field strength must be increased so that the radius of the particles orbit remains the same and the particles do not collide with the walls of the accelerator.

Quantities: G Newton's gravitational constant $(N\,m^2\,kg^{-2})$
g gravitational field strength $(N\,kg^{-1})$
E electric field strength $(N\,C^{-1})$
B magnetic flux density (T)
a centripetal acceleration $(m\,s^{-2})$ F centripetal force (N)
ϵ_0 permittivity of free space $(F\,m^{-1})$ T orbital period (s)
q, Q charge (C) m, M mass (kg)
r radius of orbit (m) v velocity $(m\,s^{-1})$

Equations: $$g = \frac{GM}{r^2} \quad E = \frac{Q}{4\pi\epsilon_0 r^2} \quad a = \frac{v^2}{r} \quad F = ma \quad v = \frac{2\pi r}{T}$$
$$F = mg \qquad F = qE \qquad F = qvB \quad r^3 \propto T^2$$

26.1 A moon of mass m moves at speed v in a circular orbit around a planet of mass M

    a) Use the equations above to obtain v in terms of G, M and r.

    b) Use the equations above to derive Kepler's Third Law: $r^3 \propto T^2$,

    c) What is the constant of proportionality r^3/T^2 in terms of G and M?

26.2 A positron of charge $+q$ and mass m enters a magnetic field B travelling at a speed v perpendicular to the direction of the magnetic field.

    a) Derive an expression for r in terms of q, B, m and v.

    b) If we now change the particle from a positron to a proton, keeping the magnetic field and the velocity of the particle the same, what would happen?

26.3 Calculate the radius of the Moon's orbit around the Earth given that Moon takes approximately 27 days to orbit the Earth and the mass of the Earth is 6.0×10^{24} kg.

26.4 Astronauts on the International Space Station appear weightless because both they and the space station have the same centripetal acceleration and therefore there is no contact force between the astronauts and the floor of the space station. They are in free-fall. What is the centripetal acceleration of the international space station in orbit at a height $h = 400$ km above the surface of the Earth?

Example – *Venus takes* 225 *Earth days to orbit the Sun at an average distance of* 1.08×10^8 *km. What is the mass of the Sun according to this data?*

$$r^3 = \frac{GM}{4\pi^2}T^2 \text{ therefore } M = \frac{4\pi^2 r^3}{GT^2}$$

$$M = \frac{4\pi^2(1.08 \times 10^{11})^3}{6.67 \times 10^{-11} \ (225 \times 24 \times 3600)^2} \approx 1.97 \times 10^{30} \text{ kg}$$

26.5 Calculate the orbital period of Jupiter in units of Earth years given that the mass of the Sun, $M = 2.0 \times 10^{30}$ kg, the mass of Jupiter, $m = 1.9 \times 10^{27}$ kg and the average radius of Jupiter's orbit around the sun is $R = 7.8 \times 10^8$ km.

26.6 Calculate the ratio of the radii of the orbits of Phobos and Deimos, which are the moons of Mars. The mass of Mars is $M = 6.4 \times 10^{23}$ kg, the mass of Phobos $m_1 = 11 \times 10^{15}$ kg and the mass of Deimos $m_2 = 1.5 \times 10^{15}$ kg. The period of Phobos's orbit is $T_1 = 7.7$ hours and of Deimos's orbit is $T_2 = 30.4$ hours.

26.7 61 Cygni is a wide binary star system. It contains two stars of nearly equal mass which orbit once around their mid point every 659 years. They are 1.26×10^{13} m apart. Assuming that the two stars have equal mass, calculate

   a) the speed of the stars,

   b) the total mass of the system.

26.8 Find an expression for the the ratio of the gravitational field to the electric field, g/E, for an electron that is in orbit at a radius r around the central proton of a hydrogen atom.

26.9 In a particle accelerator protons are accelerated in the $+x$-direction until they have a velocity of $v = 6.5 \times 10^6$ m s^{-1}. They then pass into a magnetic field of strength 0.1 T that is oriented in the $+y$-direction.

   a) In which direction do the protons accelerate when they first enter the magnetic field?

   b) What is the radius of the orbital path that the protons take?

27   Vectors and fields – between a planet and a moon

It is helpful to be able to calculate the gravitational field at points between a planet and its moon.

Example context: Satellites can be placed in orbits in complicated systems if we understand the overall gravitational field. The motion of stars in our galaxy can be used to measure the total mass of the galaxy, and thereby estimate the amount of dark matter in the galaxy.

Quantities: m mass of object (kg) F force on object (N)
M_P mass of planet (kg) r_P point – planet distance (m)
M_M mass of moon (kg) r_M point – moon distance (m)
g field at point $(N\,kg^{-1})$ R planet – moon distance (m)
g_P field at point due to planet $(N\,kg^{-1})$
g_M field at point due to moon $(N\,kg^{-1})$
All distances are measured to the centres of planets and moons.

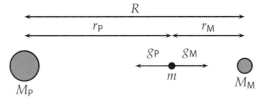

Equations: $F = mg$ $g_P = \dfrac{GM_P}{r_P^2}$ $g_M = \dfrac{GM_M}{r_M^2}$ for magnitudes only

27.1   Taking the direction $\rightarrow$ as positive, write expressions (in terms of m, M_P, M_M, r_P, r_M and G)

  a) for the force on m due to the moon,

  b) for the force on m due to the planet,

  c) for the total force F on m,

  d) for the total field g at the point where m is,

  e) relating r_P and r_M for the location where $g = 0$.

27.2   Now repeat the first four parts of question 27.1 for the situation where $r_P >$ R, and the mass m is on the far side of the moon.

27.3   Calculate g_M on the surface of the Earth nearest the Moon. The radius of the Earth is 6.37×10^6 m, the mass of the Moon is $M_M = 7.38 \times 10^{22}$ kg, and $R = 3.85 \times 10^8$ m.

Example – *Calculate the distance from the centre of a planet $M_P = 5.0 \times 10^{24}$ kg at which there is no net force on an object. The planet's moon has a mass of 5.0×10^{22} kg and orbits at a radius of 4.4×10^7 m.*

At this point total field $g = -\dfrac{GM_P}{r_P^2} + \dfrac{GM_M}{r_M^2} = 0$ so $\dfrac{M_P}{r_P^2} = \dfrac{M_M}{r_M^2}$

$$\frac{r_M}{r_P} = \sqrt{\frac{M_M}{M_S}} = \sqrt{\frac{5.0 \times 10^{22}}{5.0 \times 10^{24}}} = 0.1$$

$r_P + r_M = R$, therefore $\dfrac{r_P}{r_P} + \dfrac{r_M}{r_P} = \dfrac{R}{r_P}$. So $1 + 0.1 = \dfrac{R}{r_P}$

Therefore $r_P = \dfrac{R}{1.1} = \dfrac{4.4 \times 10^7}{1.1} = 4.0 \times 10^7$ m

27.4 For the system in the example, calculate the total field g at the locations below on the same side of the planet as the moon. Take the direction from the planet to the moon as positive. Assume that the planet and moon have radii less than 10^6 m.

    a) $r_P = 2.2 \times 10^7$ m   c) $r_P = 4.1 \times 10^7$ m

    b) $r_P = 3.9 \times 10^7$ m   d) $r_P = 1.6 \times 10^6$ m

27.5 For the Earth - Moon system, $M_P = 81 M_M$ and $R = 3.85 \times 10^8$ m.

    a) Calculate r_M / r_P for the place where $g = 0$.

    b) Evaluate r_M (for the same place) as a fraction of R.

    c) Evaluate r_P at this place.

27.6 Mars has a mass of 6.39×10^{23} kg, and its 1.06×10^{17} kg moon Phobos has an orbital radius of 9.38×10^6 m. Calculate the gravitational field strength 6.0 km from the centre of Phobos on its surface nearest to Mars. Does the field point towards or away from Mars?

27.7 The mass of the Sun is 2.00×10^{30} kg, and the Earth-Sun distance is 1.50×10^{11} m. You may also use data from questions 27.3 and 27.5. Work out the component of the field g due to the Sun and the Moon (separately) pointing towards the centre of the Earth at the locations below:

    a) at the surface of the Earth, nearest the Moon, at a full Moon,

    b) at the surface of the Earth, nearest the Sun, at a full Moon.

    c) Given your answers, what is principally responsible for the Earth's tides? The Sun or the Moon?

28 Vectors and fields – electric deflection

When a charged particle moves in a region with a uniform electric field perpendicular to its motion, it is deflected sideways and follows a parabolic path. You can calculate the deflection distance and the angle by which its velocity changes.

Example context: Some cathode ray tubes (CRTs) deflect electrons in this way to aim them at a screen, especially those used in oscilloscopes in the 20th Century.

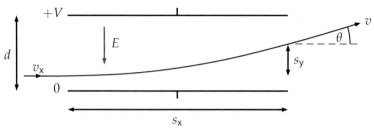

Quantities:
m mass (kg)
q charge (C)
V voltage across plates (V)
d plate separation (m)
E electric field (V m^{-1})
F_E electric force (N)
t time spent in field (s)

a_y acceleration (m s^{-2})
v_x initial speed (m s^{-1})
v_y new velocity component (m s^{-1})
v new speed (m s^{-1})
s_x length of field region (m)
s_y deflection distance (m)
θ deflection angle $(°)$

Equations:
$$E = V/d \qquad F_E = qE \qquad F_E = ma_y \qquad v_y = a_y t$$
$$s_x = v_x t \qquad s_y = \tfrac{1}{2}a_y t^2 \qquad \tan\theta = v_y/v_x \qquad v = \sqrt{v_x^2 + v_y^2}$$

28.1 Use the equations to derive expressions for
  a) a_y in terms of V, d, q and m,
  b) s_y in terms of v_x, s_x, V, d, q and m,
  c) θ in terms of v_x, s_x, V, d, q and m,
  d) s_y in terms of t, E, q and m,
  e) θ in terms of v_x, t, E, q and m.

28.2 Find F_E and a_y if $q = 1 \times 10^{-12}$ C, $m = 1 \times 10^{-20}$ kg, $V = 5$ V and $d = 0.1$ m.

28.3 Using the values from the previous question, find s_y and θ if $v_x = 5 \times 10^4 \text{ m s}^{-1}$ and $s_x = 0.2$ m.

Example – *A charge $q = 1.0 \times 10^{-17}$ C with mass 2.0×10^{-22} kg moving at 8000 m s^{-1} passes through a region of sideways electric field for 0.1 ms and is deflected by 750 μm. What is the electric field strength?*

$$s_y = \frac{1}{2}\left(\frac{qE}{m}\right)t^2 \text{ so } E = \frac{2ms_y}{qt^2} = \frac{2(2\times 10^{-22})(750 \times 10^{-6})}{(10^{-17})(10^{-4})^2} = 3.0\,V\,m^{-1}$$

28.4 Fill in the missing entries in the table below for an electron with charge 1.60×10^{-19} C and mass 9.11×10^{-31} kg.

V / V	d / m	v_x / m s^{-1}	s_x / m	s_y / m	θ / $^\circ$
0.25	0.20	4.0×10^6	1.0	(a)	(b)
(c)	0.010	7.0×10^6	0.025	2.0 mm	(d)
60 mV	1.2 cm	9.0×10^5	(e)	(f)	2.0°

28.5 Fill in the missing entries in the table below for an α-particle with charge 3.20×10^{-19} C and mass 6.64×10^{-27} kg.

E / V m^{-1}	t / s	v_x / m s^{-1}	v_y / m s^{-1}	s_y / m	θ / $^\circ$
100	5.0×10^{-6}	40 000	(a)	(b)	(c)
4.8	(d)	2.5×10^5	(e)	(f)	0.40°
(g)	14 μs	(h)	(i)	2.7 mm	7.3°

28.6 ^{23}Na$^+$ ions (mass 23 u; 1 u $= 1.66 \times 10^{-27}$ kg) are accelerated to 9600 m s^{-1} and deflected by an electric field region of length 3.0 cm between plates of separation 1.5 cm. Find the deflection distance if the plate voltage is

a) 500 mV,   b) 3.0 V,   c) 10 V.

28.7 An engineer claims electrons with initial speed 800 km s^{-1} are deflected by 45° after travelling through a 5.0 mm-wide region between plates with a voltage 150 mV between them. Find s_y and d. Is this possible?

28.8 In an oscilloscope, a deflector applies up to 1 kV between two 3.0 mm-long plates separated by 2.0 mm. Electrons with initial kinetic energy 1500 eV pass through the deflector.

a) By what angle are electrons deflected at the maximum voltage?

b) A phosphorescent screen is placed 10 cm away so that undeflected electrons hit the centre of the screen. How far from the centre of the screen can deflected electrons land?

29 Vectors and Fields - helix in magnetic field

When a charged particle moves in a region with a uniform magnetic field , it will follow a helical path, like a corkscrew or a screw. To determine the size of the helix and its pitch, you need to consider the components of velocity parallel and perpendicular to the magnetic field.

Example context: Cosmic rays spiral along our Earth's magnetic field. They then travel to our polar regions along the magnetic field lines where they collide with other particles and produce the Northern and Southern Lights.

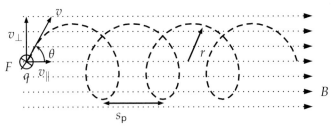

Quantities: q charge (C) v velocity $(\mathrm{m\,s^{-1}})$
                     B magnetic field (F) F force (N)
                     s_p pitch of helix (m) r radius of helix (m)
                     T period of rotation (s) m mass (kg)
                     θ angle between velocity and magnetic field $(^\circ)$
                     Subscripts $\perp$, $\parallel$ refer to perpendicular and parallel components.

Equations: $F = qv_\perp B$ $s_\mathrm{p} = v_\parallel T$ $F = m\dfrac{v_\perp^2}{r}$
                     $v_\parallel = v\cos\theta$ $v_\perp = v\sin\theta$

29.1   Use the equations to derive expressions for

        a) r in terms of m, q, v, B, and θ,

        b) T in terms of m, q, and B,

        c) v in terms of $v_\parallel$ and $v_\perp$,

        d) q/m, known as the charge to mass ratio, in terms of v, B, s_p, and θ.

Example – A charge of -1.0×10^{-17} C with mass 2.0×10^{-22} kg moving at 8000 m s^{-1} along the x-axis enters a magnetic field magnitude 510 mT. The magnetic field is at $25°$ to the x-axis. What is the force from the magnetic field on the charge?

The magnitude of the force is

$$F = qvB \sin \theta = 1 \times 10^{-17} \times 8000 \times 0.510 \times \sin(25°) = 1.7 \times 10^{-14} \, \text{N}$$

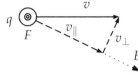

To find the direction of the force on the particle, use Fleming's left-hand rule. If the charge is negative, the force will be pointing in the opposite direction to the thumb. Here, the force is pointing out of the page.

29.2 A charged particle of mass 1.05×10^{-25} kg and charge 3.2×10^{-19} C enters a 1.45 T magnetic field with a speed of 3.2×10^6 m s^{-1}. The velocity of the particle is at an angle of $30°$ to the magnetic field. What is the radius and the pitch of the helix that the particle now follows?

29.3 An α-particle with charge to mass ratio $q/m = 4.82 \times 10^7$ C kg^{-1} is detected in a large cloud chamber with a 1.5 T magnetic field. It followed a helical path with a pitch of 44.6 cm and radius 19.5 cm. What was the kinetic energy of the α-particle?

29.4 A charged particle moves in a magnetic field. It follows a helical path with a radius 19 cm and pitch 1.20 m.

    a) At what angle to the magnetic field was the particle travelling at when it entered the magnetic field?

    b) If $q/m = 2.47 \times 10^3$ C kg^{-1} and the magnitude of the magnetic field is 1.78 T, what was the speed when the particle entered the field?

    c) What is the speed of the particle now that it is in the magnetic field?

29.5 A proton of mass 1.67×10^{-27} kg and charge 1.6×10^{-19} C enters a 500 mT magnetic field parallel to its velocity. Both are along the positive x-axis. The proton is travelling with velocity 4.3×10^7 m s^{-1}.

    a) What is the magnitude and direction of the force acting on the particle?

    b) Will it travel along a helical, circular or straight path? If the path of the proton is a helix or a circle what is the pitch and radius of the helix?

    c) The same proton now enters a 500 mT magnetic field perpendicular to its direction of travel, i.e. the magnetic field is along the positive y-axis. What will the magnitude and direction of the force acting on the particle be now?

    d) Will it travel along a helical, circular or straight path in the perpendicular field? If the path of the proton is a helix or a circle what is the pitch and radius of the helix?

30 Vectors and fields – mass spectrometer

A mass spectrometer is used to measure the mass/charge ratio of ions or particles. An understanding of electric and magnetic fields enables us to analyse the data.

Example context: the radius of the path in a magnetic field, coupled with a knowledge of the accelerating voltage, enables us to measure the mass of a carbon ion. Multiple measurements allow a measurement of the fraction of $^{14}_{6}C$ in the sample.

Quantities:
m particle mass (kg) q particle charge (C)
v particle speed (m s^{-1}) V_s velocity selector voltage (V)
V_a accelerating voltage (V) d velocity selector plate gap (m)
r path radius (m) B magnetic flux density (T)
E electric field in velocity selector $(\text{N C}^{-1} = \text{V m}^{-1})$
F_E electric force (N) F_B magnetic force (N)

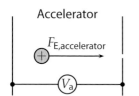
Accelerator

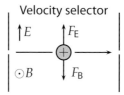
Velocity selector

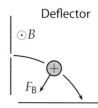
Deflector

Equations: $F = ma$ $F_E = qE$ $F_B = Bqv$ $qV_a = \frac{1}{2}mv^2$ (see page 45)

$E = \dfrac{V_s}{d}$ $a = \dfrac{v^2}{r}$

30.1 Use the equations to derive expressions for

a) the radius r of the path in the magnetic field in terms of B, v, q and m,

b) the radius r in terms of B, V_a, q and m,

c) the specific charge q/m in terms of B, r and v,

d) the specific charge q/m in terms of B, r and V_a,

e) the voltage V_s across the plates in the velocity selector so that particles of speed v are not deflected.

30.2 Calculate the speed electrons emerge from a 95 V accelerator. Assume that the electrons start from rest.

30.3 Calculate the radius of curvature of a 2.5×10^6 m s^{-1} electron in a 1.5 mT magnetic field.

30.4   Repeat question 30.3 for a proton of the same speed in the same field.

> **Example** – *Calculate the radius of curvature of a proton accelerated to 25 MV in a 0.75 T magnetic field.*
>
> We use $qV_a = \frac{1}{2}mv^2$ to calculate the speed $v = \sqrt{\dfrac{2qV_a}{m}}$
>
> $$v = \sqrt{\frac{2 \times 1.60 \times 10^{-19} \times 2.5 \times 10^7}{1.67 \times 10^{-27}}} = 6.921 \times 10^7 \text{ m s}^{-1}.$$
>
> In the magnetic field $F_B = ma$ so $Bqv = \dfrac{mv^2}{r}$ and $r = \dfrac{mv}{Bq}$
>
> $$r = \frac{1.67 \times 10^{-27} \times 6.921 \times 10^7}{0.75 \times 1.60 \times 10^{-19}} = 0.96 \text{ m to 2sf.}$$

30.5   Fill in the missing entries in the table below for a proton with $B = 2.2$ T.

V_a / V	v / m s^{-1}	r / m
	2.5×10^5	(a)
1.2×10^6	(b)	(c)
	(d)	0.014
(e)		0.12

30.6   Calculate the specific charge q/m of a particle travelling at 2.0×10^6 m s^{-1} in a magnetic field if $r = 11.9$ mm and $B = 0.175$ T.

30.7   Calculate V_s needed in a velocity selector to pass 1.6×10^6 m s^{-1} electrons in a 2.2 T magnetic field if $d = 6.5$ cm.

30.8   Protons pass through a velocity selector with $B = 1.5$ T and $d = 8.0$ cm when $V_s = 420$ kV. Calculate their speed.

30.9   Repeat question 30.8 for electrons with the same values for B, d and V_s.

30.10   Calculate the radius of the path of a $^{235}_{92}$U nucleus travelling at 4.2×10^6 m s^{-1} in a 1.25 T magnetic field. Assume that $m = 235$ u where 1 u $= 1.66 \times 10^{-27}$ kg.

30.11   A singly charged ion is accelerated by a 650 kV potential before passing into a region with a 1.25 T magnetic field. It curves with a radius of 0.322 m. Calculate its mass.

30.12   Express your mass from question 30.11 in terms of atomic mass units u where 1 u $= 1.66 \times 10^{-27}$ kg.

30.13   Calculate the radius of curve expected for a singly charged ion of $^{14}_{6}$C in the mass spectrometer of question 30.11. Assume that $m = 14$ u.

31 Deriving kinetic theory

We create a mathematical model using Newton's laws for the particles in a gas. When we have done this, we find it predicts many aspects of bulk gas behaviour correctly. To do this, we assume that the gas is an **ideal gas**.

Example context: explaining how the volume, pressure and temperature of a gas change by considering the collisions of the particles in the gas with each other and the walls of the container. This allows you to predict the thermodynamic behaviour of a gas without having to do an experiment.

Quantities:
Δ "A change in"
F force (N)
t time taken (s)
s distance travelled (m)
A area of face $\left(m^2\right)$
N number of molecules
u, v, w components of velocity in the x, y, z directions $\left(m\,s^{-1}\right)$

m mass of a particle (kg)
p momentum of a particle $\left(kg\,m\,s^{-1}\right)$
c speed of a particle $\left(m\,s^{-1}\right)$
P pressure of a gas $\left(N\,m^{-2}\,or\,Pa\right)$
V volume of gas $\left(m^3\right)$
$\overline{c^2}$ mean-square speed $\left(m^2\,s^{-2}\right)$

Equations:
$$F = \frac{\Delta mv}{\Delta t} \qquad P = \frac{F}{A}$$
$$v = \frac{s}{t} \qquad p = m \times \text{velocity}$$
$$\Delta p = p_{\text{after}} - p_{\text{before}}$$
$$a^2 = b^2 + c^2 \text{ (Pythagoras)}$$

Assumptions about ideal gases:

1. The volume of a particle is so small compared to the volume of the gas, we can ignore it.
2. There are no attractive forces between particles, only collision forces.
3. Particle movement is continuous and random.
4. Particle collisions are perfectly elastic, so there is no loss of kinetic energy.
5. Collision time is very short in comparison with the time between impacts.
6. There are enough molecules for statistics to be applied.

Example – *Consider a gas particle of mass m with speed c. We can write c in terms of 3 velocity components, u, v and w in the x, y and z directions respectively. Prove that $c^2 = u^2 + v^2 + w^2$ using Pythagoras' Theorem.*

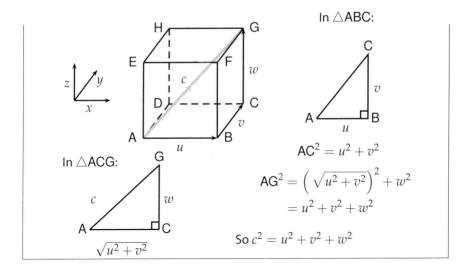

In △ABC:

$$AC^2 = u^2 + v^2$$
$$AG^2 = \left(\sqrt{u^2+v^2}\right)^2 + w^2$$
$$= u^2 + v^2 + w^2$$

So $c^2 = u^2 + v^2 + w^2$

31.A   The particle is in a box of dimensions l_x, l_y, l_z. The box represents the volume of the gas. The shaded faces represent the collisions. Write down the formula for the volume of the box V in terms of l_x, l_y and l_z.

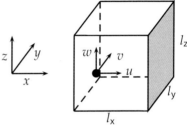

We can think of the gas as a group of N particles moving around randomly, hitting the sides of the container. As the motion is random, we expect the average speeds in different directions to be the same.

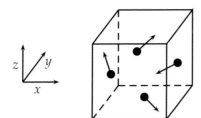

Let's consider one particle moving in the positive x direction. The particle collides with the container wall.

31.B   Write an expression for the change in momentum of the particle, Δp, in terms of m and u. Pay attention to which direction is positive.

31.C   Write an expression for the average force F_{particle} on the particle (from the wall), to cause the change in momentum of the particle. The time between collisions with the wall is Δt.

31.D Use Newton's Third Law of Motion to write down an expression for the average force, F_{wall}, of the particle on the wall over time Δt. Pay attention to the sign.

31.E Between collisions the particle will travel to the other side of the container and back again. Find an expression for Δt in terms of u and l_x.

31.F Now substitute your expression for Δt from 31.E into your equation in 31.D and simplify it. This will give you a new expression for the force of the particle on the wall, F_{wall}, in terms of m, u, and l_x.

31.G The average pressure exerted by the particle on the wall may be written as F_{wall} / A, where A is the area of the wall. Use your answer to 31.F to find an expression for the average pressure P_1 due to this one molecule in terms of u, m and:

    a) l_x, l_y, and l_z

    b) the volume, V, of the container. Use your answer from 31.A.

We now have an expression for the pressure P_1 on the container due to the collision of one particle. From here on we refer to this particle as 'particle 1' and label its speed as c_1 and its velocity components as u_1, v_1 and w_1. There are actually N particles in the gas. They each have the same mass m, but will have different velocities. For example, 'particle 2' has velocity components u_2, v_2 and w_2, has speed c_2, and will cause a pressure P_2.

31.H Up until now, we have assumed that our particle was only moving in the x direction. Does the expression for P_1 derived in question 31.G change if v_1 and w_1 are not necessarily zero?

31.I By looking at your reasoning for particle 1, write down an expression for the pressure P_2 on the same wall in terms of m, u_2, v_2, w_2 and V.

The total pressure on this wall will be the sum of the pressures due to all of the individual particles: $P = P_1 + P_2 + \ldots$.

31.J Use your expression from 31.G (b) to write the equation for total pressure P in terms of m, V, u_1, u_2 and the other x components of velocity. Assume that all the particles have the same mass, m.

31.K Find an expression for the average squared x component of velocity $\overline{u^2}$ if there are N molecules whose squared velocity components are u_1^2, u_2^2 and so on.

31.L Use your answer to 31.K to re-write the pressure from 31.J in terms of m, V, N and $\overline{u^2}$.

We now have an expression for the pressure of the particles on the right hand wall. As the particles are moving randomly, they exert the same pressure on the other walls as well.

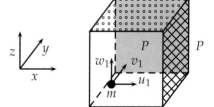

We now take into account the fact that the molecules are not just moving in the x direction.

31.M The y components of each molecule's velocity are written v_1, v_2, v_3 and so on. Use your answer to 31.K to write expressions (when there are N particles) for:

    a) the average squared y velocity component $\overline{v^2}$ and

    b) the average squared z velocity component $\overline{w^2}$.

31.N In question 31.L, you wrote an equation linking P and $\overline{u^2}$. By thinking of collisions with the back wall causing an equal pressure, write a similar equation linking P and $\overline{v^2}$. Then, by thinking of collisions with the top wall, write a similar equation linking P and $\overline{w^2}$.

31.O In the example, we saw that $c^2 = u^2 + v^2 + w^2$, where c^2 is the square speed of one molecule. Applied to particle 1 this means that $c_1^2 = u_1^2 + v_1^2 + w_1^2$. Use this information to write an equation relating $\overline{c^2}$ (the mean square speed), to $\overline{u^2}$, $\overline{v^2}$ and $\overline{w^2}$ (the mean square velocity components).

31.P Use your answers to questions 31.N and 31.O to write an equation for the pressure P in terms of the mean square speed $\overline{c^2}$.

This equation beautifully links the macroscopic behaviour of a gas (PV) with the average (square) speed of the N microscopic gas particles.

> **Exercise** – *Copy the diagram of the box and see how far you can progress with the proof without looking at all the steps. Remember:*
> 1. *1 particle*
> 2. *N particles*
> 3. *3 dimensions.*

The parts of this section are lettered A, B, C…to match with the implementation of this question online.

32 Gas laws, density and kinetic energy

We can combine the Gas Law with the molar mass equation to calculate the density of a gas if we know the molar or molecular mass. We can also relate the temperature of a gas to the average kinetic energy of its molecules.

Gas density is important as it will determine whether the gas will rise or fall relative to the medium it is in, for example in a hot air balloon: the hot air in the balloon is less dense than the air surrounding the balloon. Our questions here also show the link between temperature and molecular energy for a gas.

It is useful to re-write the kinetic theory equation derived in section 31 in terms of gas density.

Quantities:
P pressure (N m^{-2})
V volume of a gas (m^3)
T temperature (K)
m mass of particle (kg)
ρ density of a gas (kg m^{-3})
M_M molar mass (kg mol^{-1})

n number of moles of gas (mol)
M total mass of gas (kg)
N number of particles in a gas
$\overline{c^2}$ mean-square speed $(\text{m}^2 \text{ s}^{-2})$
m_u molecular mass (u)
$\overline{K}$ mean molecule kinetic energy (J)

Equations:
$$PV = nRT \qquad n = \frac{M}{M_M} \qquad PV = \frac{Nm\overline{c^2}}{3} \qquad n = \frac{N}{N_A} \qquad \rho = \frac{M}{V}$$

$$PV = Nk_B T \qquad \overline{K} = \tfrac{1}{2}m\overline{c^2} \qquad m_u = \frac{m}{1.66 \times 10^{-27} \text{ kg}}$$

32.1 Use the equations above to derive expressions for

  a) P in terms of M, M_M, V, R and T,

  b) ρ in terms of M_M, P, R and T,

  c) ρ in terms of m, P, k_B and T,

  d) ρ in terms of P and $\overline{c^2}$,

  e) $\overline{K}$ in terms of k_B and T.

Example 1 – *What is the density of carbon dioxide gas (CO_2) at a pressure of 110 kPa and a temperature of 30 °C? The molar mass of C is 12 g mol^{-1} and the molar mass of O is 16 g mol^{-1}. Remember to convert g to kg.*
The molar mass of the molecule is $(12 + 2 \times 16)$ g $= 0.044$ kg
$T = 273 + 30 = 303$ K

$$\rho = \frac{M_M P}{RT} = \frac{0.044 \times 110 \times 10^3}{8.31 \times 303} = 1.9222 \text{ kg m}^{-3} = 1.9 \text{ kg m}^{-3} \text{ (2 s.f.)}$$

32.2 What is the density of a sulfuric acid gas cloud on Venus if the temperature is $467\ °C$ and the pressure is 9308 kPa? The chemical formula for sulfuric acid is H_2SO_4.

Element	Molar mass / g mol^{-1}
H	1
S	32
O	16

32.3 Use your answer to 32.1 to complete the following table containing information on different gases: (give your answers to 2 s.f.)

Chemical formula	Molecular mass / u	Temperature / K	Pressure / kPa	Density / kg m^{-3}
NO_2	46	500	115	(a)
HCl	36.5	(b)	120	277
NH_3	17	723	(c)	57.3

Example 2 – *What is the density of a gas at a pressure of 101 kPa if the root mean square velocity $c_{rms} = \sqrt{\overline{c^2}}$ of the particles is 500 m s^{-1}?*

$$\rho = \frac{3P}{\overline{c^2}} = \frac{3 \times 101 \times 10^3}{500^2} = 1.212 \text{ kg m}^{-3} = 1.21 \text{ kg m}^{-3} \text{ (3 s.f.)}$$

This is a typical value for air at room temperature.

32.4 What is the density of a gas at a pressure of 150 kPa if the mean square speed of the particles is 9.0×10^4 m^{2}s^{-2}?

32.5 What is the pressure needed for a gas of density 1.2 kg m^{-3} to have a root mean square speed of 330 m s^{-1}?

32.6 Calculate the mean kinetic energy of molecules in a gas at $15\ °C$.

32.7 Calculate the temperature at which the mean molecular kinetic energy is 1.60×10^{-21} J.

32.8 Within a gas mixture at equilibrium, the mean kinetic energy of each type of molecule is the same. This is because the temperature is uniform. In a mixture of helium ($m = 4.00$ u) and nitrogen ($m = 28.0$ u),

a) state which molecules typically move faster, and

b) calculate the ratio $\overline{c^2_{helium}} / \overline{c^2_{nitrogen}}$.

33 Capacitors and resistors

A capacitor can be charged or discharged gradually by connecting it in series with a resistor (and if charging, a voltage source). The voltages and currents in the circuit are decaying exponential functions of time.

Example context: Circuits containing capacitors and resistors in series are important in electronics applications, including signal processing and timing. You can calculate the capacitor charge, voltages and current in the circuit at any time.

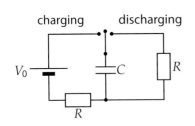
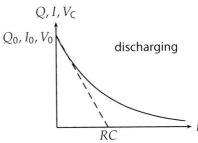

Quantities:
R resistance (Ω)
C capacitance (F)
t time (s)
Q charge on capacitor (C)
I current in circuit (A)

V_C voltage across capacitor (V)
V_R voltage across resistor (V)
V_0 initial or max voltage (V)
Q_0 initial or max charge (C)
I_0 initial current (A)

Equations:

$Q = CV_C$	$V_R = IR$	$I = I_0 e^{-t/RC}$
When discharging:	$V_C = V_R$	$V_C = V_0 e^{-t/RC}$
When charging:	$V_C + V_R = V_0$	$V_C = V_0 \left(1 - e^{-t/RC}\right)$

33.1 Use the equations to write down expressions for

a) the charge Q versus time, when discharging;

b) the charge Q versus time, when charging;

c) the initial charge Q_0 in terms of V_0 and C;

d) the voltage V_R across the resistor versus time, when discharging;

e) the voltage V_R across the resistor versus time, when charging;

f) Q in terms of I when discharging;

g) Q in terms of $dQ/dt = -I$ when discharging;

h) I_0 in terms of V_0 and R when discharging;

i) I_0 in terms of Q_0, R and C when discharging;

j) the time to completely discharge if the current were constant at I_0;

k) the fraction of Q_0 still on the capacitor after a time RC.

33.2 Find Q_0 and I_0 if $R = 200\ \Omega$, $C = 0.0010$ F and $V_0 = 5.0$ V when discharging.

33.3 A 47 μF capacitor discharges through a resistor. The initial charge on the capacitor is 9.4 μC and the initial current is 8.0 mA. Find the value of the resistor.

Example – A 600 μF capacitor is charged to 9.0 V and then discharged through a 70 kΩ resistor. How much charge is on the capacitor after 100 s?

$$Q = CV_C = CV_0 e^{-t/RC} = (6 \times 10^{-4}) \times 9 \times e^{-100/(7 \times 10^4 \times 6 \times 10^{-4})} = 500\ \mu C$$

33.4 Fill in the missing entries in the table below for a capacitor discharging from an initial voltage of 10 V.

R/Ω	C/F	t/s	Q/C	V/V	I/A
550	8.0×10^{-3}	5.0		(a)	
550	8.0×10^{-3}	15		(b)	
2.2 MΩ	3.0×10^{-5}	10	(c)		(d)
2.2 MΩ	3.0×10^{-5}	20	(e)		(f)
2.2 MΩ	3.0×10^{-5}	50	(g)		(h)

33.5 A capacitor with $C = 10$ nF and initial charge 1.5×10^{-7} C is discharged through a resistor with $R = 10$ MΩ. What is the current after 0.25 s?

33.6 An initially uncharged 0.0020 F capacitor is connected to a 6.0 V battery via a 9.0 Ω resistor. How much charge has entered the capacitor after the first 0.02 s?

33.7 In a timing circuit, an initially uncharged 0.10 mF capacitor is connected to a 4.5 V source through a 80 Ω resistor.

a) What is the voltage across the capacitor after 5 ms?

b) After 5 ms, the capacitor is then disconnected from the source and connected across another 80 Ω resistor to discharge. What is the voltage across the resistor after another 5 ms?

34 Exponential attenuation with distance

It is helpful to be able to calculate the intensity of radiation that penetrates an absorbing medium as a function of distance.

Example context: X-ray radiation is able to penetrate human tissues, but as the tissues are made thicker, less X-ray radiation is able to penetrate. The relationship between the intensity of radiation that penetrates the tissue and the tissue thickness is an exponential attenuation.

Quantities: I detected intensity $(\mathrm{W\,m^{-2}})$ I_0 starting intensity $(\mathrm{W\,m^{-2}})$
μ attenuation coefficient $(\mathrm{m^{-1}})$ x absorber thickness (m)
ρ density $(\mathrm{kg\,m^{-3}})$ $x_{1/2}$ halving thickness (m)
m mass (kg) V volume $(\mathrm{m^3})$

Equations: $I = I_0\,e^{-\mu x}$ $\lambda = \dfrac{\ln(2)}{x_{1/2}}$ $\rho = \dfrac{m}{V}$
If $B = e^a$ then $a = \ln(B)$ $\ln\left(B^{-1}\right) = -\ln(B)$

34.1 Use the equations to derive expressions for

      a) the thickness x needed for I_0 to attenuate to I in terms of μ,

      b) the halving thickness $x_{1/2}$ of I in terms of μ,

      c) the thickness x for I_0 to attenuate to I in terms of $x_{1/2}$.

Example 1 – *Calculate the halving thickness $x_{1/2}$ for human muscle tissue for medical X-rays, where $\mu = 1.91\ cm^{-1}$.*

$x_{1/2} = \frac{1}{\mu}\ln 2 = \frac{1}{1.91}\ln 2 = 0.363$ cm

---

34.2 Fill in the missing entries in the table below.

$I\,/\,\mathrm{W\,m^{-2}}$	$I_0\,/\,\mathrm{W\,m^{-2}}$	$\mu\,/\,\mathrm{cm^{-1}}$	$x_{1/2}\,/\,\mathrm{cm}$	$x\,/\,\mathrm{cm}$
(a)	1.06	1.91		2.00
0.050	(b)		0.400	2.00
		(c)	0.300	
0.100	0.500		(d)	1.00
5.00×10^{-3}	0.750	2.10		(e)

Example 2 – *The medical x-ray mass attenuation coefficient (μ/ρ) for bone tissue is $1.80\ cm^2\ g^{-1}$. Bone has a density of $1300\ kg\ m^{-3}$. Calculate the halving thickness $x_{1/2}$ of bone.*

$1300\ \text{kg m}^{-3} = 1.300\ \text{g cm}^{-3}$.

So $\mu = 1.80\ \text{cm}^2\ \text{g}^{-1} \times 1.300\ \text{g cm}^{-3} = 2.34\ \text{cm}^{-1}$

$$x_{1/2} = \frac{\ln 2}{\mu} = \frac{\ln 2}{2.34} = 0.296\ \text{cm}$$

34.3 A patient receives a chest X-ray. The thickness of tissue through which the X-rays pass is 20.0 cm. The average mass attenuation coefficient of the tissue is $1.8\ \text{cm}^2\ \text{g}^{-1}$, and the average density is $1108\ \text{kg m}^{-3}$.

    a) Calculate the attenuation coefficient μ.

    b) If $1.00\ \text{fW m}^{-2}$ radiation must be incident on the X-ray film during the exposure in order to produce an image, calculate the necessary intensity of radiation incident on the patient. $1\ \text{fW} = 10^{-15}\ \text{W}$

    c) Certain photographic film can be used to detect X-ray radiation intensities that are 1% of that in (b). Calculate the necessary intensity of radiation incident on the patient when this type of film is used.

34.4 A patient receives an arm X-ray. X-rays that do not pass through bone pass through 5.00 cm of muscular tissue ($\mu = 1.90\ \text{cm}^{-1}$). Those that do pass through bone pass through 1.00 cm of bone tissue right in the centre of the arm ($\mu = 2.30\ \text{cm}^{-1}$). The medical X-ray produces radiation of intensity $1.00\ \text{W m}^{-2}$.

    a) Calculate the intensity of X-ray radiation that passes through the muscular tissue (and does not pass through bone) I_m.

    b) Calculate the intensity of X-ray radiation that passes through the arm tissue, including the bone in the centre I_b.

    c) Calculate the ratio of the radiation that passes through the arm tissue (including the bone) compared to the arm tissue without the bone I_b/I_m as a percentage.

34.5 In question 34.4 you assumed that the 1.00 cm of bone was exactly in the centre of the arm. Repeat the calculation assuming that the bone is the first tissue encountered (i.e. 1.00 cm of bone followed by 4.00 cm of muscular tissue). Calculate the ratio I_b/I_m as a percentage. What do you notice?

35 Exponential decay – using logarithms

It is helpful to be able to calculate the time taken for a particular point to be reached in an exponential decay.

Example context: the age of many archaeological artifacts can be worked out from the fraction of $^{14}_{6}C$ in the object's carbon. Equally the thickness of shielding needed to protect a person from unnecessary exposure to X rays or γ rays can be worked out from the reduction in intensity required.

Quantities:	t time (s)	N number of nuclei (no unit)
	I intensity (Wm^{-2})	x thickness (m)
	V voltage (V)	λ decay constant (s^{-1})
	R resistance (Ω)	C capacitance (F)
	$T_{1/2}$ halving time (s)	μ attenuation co-efficient (m^{-1})
	$_0$ means initial value	X decaying quantity (various)

Equations: $\quad X = X_0\, e^{-\lambda t} \quad V = V_0\, e^{-t/RC} \qquad I = I_0\, e^{-\mu x} \qquad A = \lambda N$

$\qquad\qquad$ If $B = e^a$ then $a = \ln(B) \qquad \ln\left(B^{-1}\right) = -\ln(B) \qquad \lambda = \dfrac{\ln(2)}{T_{1/2}}$

35.1 Use the equations to derive expressions for

a) the time t taken for X_0 to decay to X in terms of λ,

b) the halving time $T_{1/2}$ of V in terms of R and C,

c) the time t taken for X_0 to decay to X in terms of $T_{1/2}$,

d) the distance x taken for I_0 to reduce to I in terms of μ,

e) the halving distance of $I = I_0 e^{-\mu x}$ in terms of μ.

Example – *Calculate the time taken for 60% of the ^3_1H in an emergency exit sign to decay.* $T_{1/2} = 12.4$ *years*

If 60% has decayed, 40% remains, so $\dfrac{N}{N_0} = 0.40$. We will work in years.

We use $N = N_0\, e^{-\lambda t}$, so $\dfrac{N}{N_0} = 0.40 = e^{-\lambda t}$, which means $\ln(0.4) = -\lambda t$.

$t = \dfrac{\ln(0.40)}{-\lambda} = -\ln(0.40) \times \left(\dfrac{T_{1/2}}{\ln(2)}\right) = -12.4 \times \dfrac{\ln 0.4}{\ln 2} = 16.4$ years.

35.2 How much time is taken for 7.0% of a radioactive rock (containing uranium) to decay if $T_{1/2} = 4.5 \times 10^9$ years?

35.3 A patient is injected with a radioisotope with a six hour half life. How much time must they wait before the activity has reduced to on thousandth of its original value?

35.4 A powerful painkiller has a biological half life of three hours. This means that if one dose is given to a patient, 50% of it will remain in the patient three hours later, and only 25% of it will still be in the patient three hours after that. The remainder will have been excreted. If the quantity of the painkiller must not go below 80% of its initial value, how often must the medication be given?

35.5 The attenuation co-efficient of lead for many gamma rays is $\mu = 1.4 \, \text{cm}^{-1}$.

    a) What fraction of gamma rays will be absorbed by 2.5 mm of lead?

    b) If you wish to reduce gamma ray intensity by 10^4, what thickness of lead would be needed?

35.6 The attenuation co-efficient for neutrinos in lead is approximately $\mu = 7 \times 10^{-17} \, \text{m}^{-1}$. Calculate the thickness of lead needed to stop one quarter of the neutrinos flowing out from the Sun.

35.7 Optical filters are labelled with their optical density (OD). An OD1 filter only allows $10\% = 10^{-1}$ of light to pass. An OD2 filter allows $1\% = 10^{-2}$ of the light to pass. To view a Solar eclipse safely, you need at least OD5. I have an OD1 filter made of a plastic material which is 0.24 mm thick.

    a) Calculate the attenuation co-efficient μ in mm^{-1}.

    b) What thickness of material is needed to make an OD2 filter?

    c) What would be the thickness of material to block half of the light?

    d) What thickness of material is needed in safety glasses for watching a Solar Eclipse?

35.8 In the inflationary model of the early universe, the universe expanded exponentially $L = L_0 \, e^{+\lambda t}$ by a factor of 10^{27} in approximately 10^{-33}s.

    a) Calculate the constant λ in s^{-1}.

    b) How long did it take for the universe to get a million times larger?

35.9 The capacitor in a timer is charged quickly to a battery voltage of 5.3 V. It then discharges through a resistor. The charge and the voltage drop to one third of their initial value in ten seconds. How long does it take the capacitor voltage to fall from the original value to 2.56 V?

Solutions to first questions

1 Gravitational potential and kinetic energy

(a) $E_{T,\text{before}} = E_{T,\text{after}}$, so $E_{P,\text{before}} = E_{K,\text{after}}$, and $mgh_0 = \frac{1}{2}mv_1^2$.

Therefore $v_1 = \sqrt{2gh_0}$

(b) $E_{T,\text{before}} = E_{T,\text{after}}$, so $E_{P,\text{before}} + E_{K,\text{before}} = E_{P,\text{after}} + E_{K,\text{after}}$

So $mgh_0 + \frac{1}{2}mv_0^2 = mgh_1 + \frac{1}{2}mv_1^2$, and $v_1 = \sqrt{2g(h_0 - h_1) + v_0^2}$

(c) $E_{T,\text{before}} = E_{T,\text{after}}$, so $E_{K,\text{before}} = E_{P,\text{after}}$, and $\frac{1}{2}mv_0^2 = mgh_1$.

Therefore $h_1 = \dfrac{v_0^2}{2g}$

(d) $E_{T,\text{before}} = E_{T,\text{after}}$, so $E_{P,\text{before}} + E_{K,\text{before}} = E_{P,\text{after}}$

So $mgh_0 + \frac{1}{2}mv_0^2 = mgh_1$, and $h_1 = h_0 + \dfrac{v_0^2}{2g}$

(e) $E_{T,\text{after}} = \eta E_{T,\text{before}}$, so $E_{P,\text{after}} = \eta E_{P,\text{before}}$, and $mgh_1 = \eta mgh_0$.

Therefore $h_1 = \eta h_0$

(f) $E_{T,\text{after}} = \eta E_{T,\text{before}}$, so $E_{K,\text{after}} = \eta E_{K,\text{before}}$, and $\frac{1}{2}mv_1^2 = \frac{1}{2}\eta mv_0^2$.

Therefore $v_1 = \sqrt{\eta}\, v_0$

2 Gravitational, elastic and kinetic energy

(a) $E_T = E_K + E_{GP} + E_{EP} = \frac{1}{2}mv^2 - mgx + \frac{1}{2}kx^2$

(b) $kx_B = mg$ so $x_B = \dfrac{mg}{k}$

(c) $E_B = E_{GP} + E_{EP} = -mgx_B + \frac{1}{2}kx_B^2 = -\dfrac{m^2g^2}{k} + \dfrac{k}{2}\dfrac{m^2g^2}{k^2} = -\dfrac{m^2g^2}{2k}$

(d) $E_T = 0$ and $E_K = 0$, so $0 = E_{GP} + E_{EP} = -mgx + \frac{1}{2}kx^2$

$= x\left(\frac{1}{2}kx - mg\right)$ so $x = \dfrac{2mg}{k}$

(e) $E_{GP} + E_{EP} = -mgx + \frac{1}{2}kx^2 = -mg\left(x_B + y\right) + \frac{1}{2}k\left(x_B + y\right)^2$

$$= -mg\left(\frac{mg}{k} + y\right) + \frac{k}{2}\left(\frac{mg}{k} + y\right)^2$$

$$= -\frac{m^2g^2}{k} - mgy + \frac{m^2g^2}{2k} + mgy + \frac{ky^2}{2}$$

$$= \frac{ky^2}{2} - \frac{m^2g^2}{2k} = \frac{ky^2}{2} + E_B$$

3 Momentum and kinetic energy

(a) $p = mv$ so $v = \dfrac{p}{m}$. Therefore $E = \dfrac{m}{2}v^2 = \dfrac{m}{2}\left(\dfrac{p}{m}\right)^2 = \dfrac{p^2}{2m}$

(b) $E = \dfrac{mv^2}{2}$ so $v = \sqrt{\dfrac{2E}{m}}$. Now $p = mv = m\sqrt{\dfrac{2E}{m}} = \sqrt{\dfrac{2Em^2}{m}} = \sqrt{2mE}$

(c) $p = \sqrt{2mE} = \sqrt{2mqV}$ as $E = qV$

(d) $\lambda = \dfrac{h}{p} = \dfrac{h}{\sqrt{2mqV}}$

4 Elastic collisions

(a) $p_0 + P_0 = p_1 + P_1$ so $mv_0 + 0 = mv_1 + MV_1$ and $V_1 = \dfrac{m\left(v_0 - v_1\right)}{M}$

(b) $p_0 + P_0 = p_1 + P_1$ so $mv_0 + 0 = 0 + mV_1$ and $V_1 = v_0$

Part (b) could also be completed using energy conservation.

For the third and optional part (c), the algebra is much more complicated, but we show it so that you can see why approach and separation speeds are the same in elastic collisions. Remember that r is defined as the approach speed $(v - V = r)$, so $v = V + r$.

(c) $P + p = MV + mv = MV + m\left(V + r\right) = \left(M + m\right)V + mr$

$\left(P + p\right)^2 = \left(M + m\right)^2 V^2 + 2\left(M + m\right)mrV + m^2r^2$

$K + k = \dfrac{MV^2}{2} + \dfrac{mv^2}{2} = \dfrac{M^2V^2 + MmV^2 + m^2v^2 + Mmv^2}{2\left(M + m\right)}$

$$K + k = \frac{M^2V^2 + MmV^2 + m^2\left(V+r\right)^2 + Mm\left(V+r\right)^2}{2\left(M+m\right)}$$

$$= \frac{M^2V^2 + 2MmV^2 + m^2V^2 + 2m^2Vr + m^2r^2 + 2MmVr + Mmr^2}{2\left(M+m\right)}$$

$$= \frac{\left(M+m\right)^2V^2 + 2\left(M+m\right)mVr + m^2r^2 + Mmr^2}{2\left(M+m\right)}$$

$$= \frac{\left(P+p\right)^2 + Mmr^2}{2\left(M+m\right)}$$

$$= \frac{\left(P+p\right)^2}{2\left(M+m\right)} + \frac{Mm}{2\left(M+m\right)}r^2$$

In an elastic collision $k + K$ will be the same before and after the collision. As the total momentum $p + P$ will also be conserved, it follows that r^2 will not change either. Therefore $|r_1| = |r_0|$, so for a one-dimensional collision, $r_1 = \pm r_0$. In the $r_1 = r_0$ case, nothing has changed (there has been no collision), so in collisions $r_1 = -r_0$. In other words, when an elastic collision is viewed from the perspective of one object, the other object bounces off it at the same speed as it arrived.

5 Vectors and motion – relative motion

(a) $v_{REL} = v_A - v_T$

(b) $v_{REL} = \dfrac{s_0}{T} \longrightarrow T = \dfrac{s_0}{v_{REL}} = \dfrac{s_0}{v_A - v_T}$

(c) $s = s_0 - \left(v_A - v_T\right)t$

6 Vectors and motion – projectiles

(a) $v_y^2 = u_y^2 + 2a_ys_y$ using the vertical components of the vectors.

$s_y = -h$ when $v_y = 0$ and $a_y = g$ (downwards is positive)

$u_y = -u\sin\theta$ (as upwards is negative)

$-h = \dfrac{v_y^2 - u_y^2}{2a_y} = \dfrac{0 - u^2\sin^2\theta}{2g}$

$h = \dfrac{u^2\sin^2\theta}{2g}$

(b)   Analysing motion from high point to end $s_y = h + D$, $u_y = 0$, $a_y = g$

$$v_{y,\text{final}}^2 = u_y^2 + 2a_y s_y = 0 + 2g\,(h + D)\text{, so } v_{y,\text{final}} = \sqrt{2g\,(h + D)}$$

(c)   Using $v_y = u_y + a_y t$ over the whole motion, $v_{y,\text{final}} = -u\sin\theta + gT$

$$T = \frac{v_{y,\text{final}} + u\sin\theta}{g} = \frac{\sqrt{2g\,(h + D)} + u\sin\theta}{g}$$

$$= \frac{\sqrt{u^2\sin^2\theta + 2gD} + u\sin\theta}{g}$$

(d) $u_x = v_x$ because $a_x = 0$

$$R = u_x T = u\cos\theta \times \frac{\sqrt{u^2\sin^2\theta + 2gD} + u\sin\theta}{g}$$

7 Photon flux for an LED

(a) $I = \dfrac{\text{charge}}{t} = \dfrac{ne}{t} = \dfrac{n}{t} \cdot e = \Phi_q e$

(b) $V = \dfrac{E}{e} = \dfrac{hc}{\lambda} \cdot \dfrac{1}{e} = \dfrac{hc}{e\lambda}$

(c) $P = IV = \Phi_q e \cdot \dfrac{hc}{e\lambda} = \Phi_q \dfrac{hc}{\lambda}$

8 Potential dividers with LEDs

(a) $V = IR$ so $R = \dfrac{V}{I} = \dfrac{\varepsilon - V_{\text{LED}}}{I}$

(b) $R = \dfrac{\varepsilon - V_{\text{LED}}}{I} = \dfrac{\varepsilon}{I} - \dfrac{hc}{Ie\lambda}$

9 Current division

(a) $V = I_C R_{\text{parallel}} = I_C \left(R_1^{-1} + R_2^{-1} \right)^{-1} = \dfrac{I_C}{R_1^{-1} + R_2^{-1}}$

(b) $I_1 = \dfrac{V}{R_1} = VR_1^{-1} = \dfrac{I_C R_1^{-1}}{R_1^{-1} + R_2^{-1}}$

(c) $\quad \dfrac{I_1}{I_C} = I_1 \times \dfrac{1}{I_C} = \dfrac{I_C R_1^{-1}}{R_1^{-1} + R_2^{-1}} \times \dfrac{1}{I_C} = \dfrac{R_1^{-1}}{R_1^{-1} + R_2^{-1}}$

(d) $\quad G_1 = \dfrac{I_1}{V} = \dfrac{1}{R_1} = R_1^{-1}$

(e) $\quad G_C = G_1 + G_2 = R_1^{-1} + R_2^{-1}$

(f) $\quad \dfrac{G_1}{G_C} = \dfrac{R_1^{-1}}{R_1^{-1} + R_2^{-1}}$

We hope you noticed that $\dfrac{G_1}{G_C} = \dfrac{I_1}{I_C}$. If one resistor has two thirds of the con-ductance, it will carry two thirds of the current.

10 Power in a potential divider

(a) $\quad I = \dfrac{\epsilon}{\text{Circuit resistance}} = \dfrac{\epsilon}{R + r}$

(b) $\quad V = IR = \dfrac{\epsilon}{R + r} \times R = \dfrac{\epsilon R}{R + r}$

(c) $\quad P = IV = \dfrac{\epsilon}{R + r} \times \dfrac{\epsilon R}{R + r} = \dfrac{\epsilon^2 R}{(R + r)^2}$

(d) $\quad \eta = \dfrac{P}{I\epsilon} = P \times \dfrac{1}{\epsilon I} = \dfrac{\epsilon^2 R}{(R + r)^2} \times \dfrac{1}{\epsilon \times \epsilon / (R + r)} = \dfrac{R}{R + r}$

11 Path and phase difference

(a) $\quad \Delta\phi = \dfrac{\Delta L}{\lambda} \times 360° = \dfrac{d \sin\theta}{\lambda} \times 360°$

(b) $\quad \sin\theta = \dfrac{\Delta L}{d} = \dfrac{n\lambda}{d}$ for constructive interference

(c) $\quad \sin\theta = \dfrac{n\lambda}{d} = \dfrac{n\lambda}{1\,\text{mm}/N} = \dfrac{nN\lambda}{1 \times 10^{-3}\,\text{m}}$

(d) $\quad \sin\theta = \dfrac{nN\lambda}{1 \times 10^{-3}\,\text{m}} = \dfrac{nN\,(v/f)}{1 \times 10^{-3}\,\text{m}} = \dfrac{nNv}{1 \times 10^{-3}\,\text{m} \times f}$

(e) $\quad y = D\tan\theta \approx D\sin\theta = D \times \dfrac{n\lambda}{d} = \dfrac{1 \times \lambda D}{d} = \dfrac{\lambda D}{d}$

(f) $\quad y = D\tan\theta \approx D\sin\theta = D \times \dfrac{n\lambda}{d} = \dfrac{5 \times (v/f)\,D}{d} = \dfrac{5vD}{df}$

(g) $\quad \Delta L = \left(\tfrac{1}{2}D + y\right) - \left(\tfrac{1}{2}D - y\right) = 2y$

12 Diffraction, interference and multiple slits

(a) $L_2^2 = D^2 + \left(\dfrac{1}{2}d\right)^2$ therefore $L_2 = \sqrt{D^2 + \dfrac{d^2}{4}}$

$L_1^2 = D^2 + \left(\dfrac{3}{2}d\right)^2$ therefore $L_1 = \sqrt{D^2 + \dfrac{9d^2}{4}}$

(b) $L_2 - L_1 = \dfrac{1}{2}\lambda$

(c) $\sqrt{D^2 + \dfrac{9d^2}{4}} - \sqrt{D^2 + \dfrac{d^2}{4}} = \dfrac{1}{2}\lambda$

13 Reflection and refraction – angle of acceptance and prisms

(a) $n_A \sin\theta_1 = n_G \sin\theta_2$ therefore

$$\theta_2 = \sin^{-1}\left(\frac{n_A}{n_G}\sin\theta_1\right)$$

(b) $n_A \sin\theta_1 = n_G \sin\theta_2$ and $\theta_3 = \alpha - \theta_2$ therefore

$$\theta_3 = \alpha - \sin^{-1}\left(\frac{n_A}{n_G}\sin\theta_1\right)$$

(c) $n_A \sin\theta_4 = n_G \sin\theta_3$

$$= n_G \sin\left[\alpha - \sin^{-1}\left(\frac{n_A}{n_G}\sin\theta_1\right)\right] \quad \text{therefore}$$

$$\theta_4 = \sin^{-1}\left\{\frac{n_G}{n_A}\sin\left[\alpha - \sin^{-1}\left(\frac{n_A}{n_G}\sin\theta_1\right)\right]\right\}$$

(Or, more sensibly, do it in three stages, as it is done in the example.)

14 Optical path

(a) $\Delta\phi = \dfrac{\Delta\ell}{\lambda} \times 360° = \dfrac{\ell - x}{\lambda} \times 360°$

(b) $\Delta\phi = \dfrac{\Delta\ell}{\lambda} \times 360° = \dfrac{\ell - x}{\lambda} \times 360° = \dfrac{n \cdot x - x}{\lambda} \times 360° = \dfrac{(n-1)x}{\lambda} \times 360°$

(c) $180° = \dfrac{(n-1)x}{\lambda} \times 360°$ therefore $\dfrac{1}{2} = \dfrac{(n-1)x}{\lambda}$ so $x = \dfrac{\lambda}{2(n-1)}$

15 Standing waves on a string

(a) $f_1 = \dfrac{c}{\lambda} = \dfrac{\sqrt{\dfrac{T}{\mu}}}{\lambda} = \dfrac{1}{\lambda}\sqrt{\dfrac{T}{\mu}}$

(b) $f_1 = \dfrac{1}{\lambda}\sqrt{\dfrac{T}{\mu}} = \dfrac{1}{2\ell}\sqrt{\dfrac{T}{\mu}}$

(c) $f_n = \dfrac{c}{\lambda} = \dfrac{\sqrt{\dfrac{T}{\mu}}}{\dfrac{2\ell}{n}} = \dfrac{n}{2\ell}\sqrt{\dfrac{T}{\mu}}$

16 Inverse square intensity

(a) Area illuminated is $A_{\text{sphere}} = 4\pi r^2$, so $I = \dfrac{P}{A_{\text{sphere}}} = \dfrac{P}{4\pi r^2}$

(b) Using (a) $I = \dfrac{P}{4\pi r^2}$ so $r^2 = \dfrac{P}{4\pi I}$ and $r = \sqrt{\dfrac{P}{4\pi I}}$

(c) $P = I_1 A_1 = I_2 A_2$, so $I_1 \times 4\pi r_1^2 = I_2 \times 4\pi r_2^2$, so $I_2 = \dfrac{I_1 r_1^2}{r_2^2}$

In (c) we assumed that the radiation spread equally in all directions (so $A = 4\pi r^2$). The reasoning is also true for radiation which spreads in all **relevant** directions. In this case, P will not be the power of the source, but the power of a source which could shine this brightly in all directions.

17 Banked tracks for turning

(a) Resolving vertically, $N\cos\theta = mg$, so $N = \dfrac{mg}{\cos\theta}$

(b) $\tan\theta = \dfrac{\text{opp}}{\text{adj}} = \dfrac{mv^2/r}{mg} = \dfrac{v^2}{rg}$. So, $v = \sqrt{rg\tan\theta}$

(c) $t_p = \dfrac{2\pi r}{v} = \dfrac{2\pi r}{\sqrt{rg\tan\theta}} = 2\pi\sqrt{\dfrac{r}{g\tan\theta}}$

(d)   By Pythagoras: $N = \sqrt{(mg)^2 + \left(\dfrac{mv^2}{r}\right)^2} = mg\sqrt{1 + \dfrac{v^4}{r^2 g^2}}$

(e) $a = \dfrac{v^2}{r} = \dfrac{v}{r} \times v = \omega v$

(f)   Resolving horizontally, $N\sin\theta = mv^2/r = m\,(r\omega)^2 /r = mr\omega^2$
Resolving vertically, $N\cos\theta = mg$.

Dividing, $\tan\theta = \dfrac{N\sin\theta}{N\cos\theta} = \dfrac{r\omega^2}{g}$. Hence, $\omega = \sqrt{\dfrac{g}{r}\tan\theta}$

18   Conical pendulum

(a)   Resolve (H): $T\sin\phi = mr\omega^2$ and (V): $T\cos\phi = mg$. Divide the equations,

$\dfrac{T\sin\phi}{T\cos\phi} = \dfrac{mr\omega^2}{mg}$.   So, $\tan\phi = \dfrac{r\omega^2}{g}$. $\omega = \sqrt{\dfrac{g}{r}\tan\phi}$

(b) $t_p = \dfrac{2\pi r}{v} = \dfrac{2\pi}{\omega}$.   So, $t_p = 2\pi\sqrt{\dfrac{r}{g\tan\phi}}$

(c)   Resolving, $T\sin\phi = ma$ and $T\cos\phi = mg$. Then $\quad a = g\tan\phi$

(d)   From the horizontal equation in (c), $a = \dfrac{T\sin\phi}{m}$

(e)   From the equations in (a), squaring and adding,
$(T\cos\phi)^2 + (T\sin\phi)^2 = T^2(\cos^2\phi + \sin^2\phi) = T^2 = (mg)^2 + (mr\omega)^2$.

Then, $T = mg\sqrt{1 + \dfrac{r^2\omega^4}{g^2}}$

(f)   Using Pythagoras, $\cos\phi = \dfrac{\text{adj}}{\text{hyp}} = \dfrac{\sqrt{\ell^2 - r^2}}{\ell} = \sqrt{1 - \dfrac{r^2}{\ell^2}}$

(g) $\tan\phi = \dfrac{r\omega^2}{g}$ and also $\tan\phi = \dfrac{r}{\sqrt{\ell^2 - r^2}}$. Equating, $\omega^2 = \dfrac{g}{\sqrt{\ell^2 - r^2}}$

(h) $\tan^2 \phi = \dfrac{\sin^2 \phi}{\cos^2 \phi} = \dfrac{1 - \cos^2 \phi}{\cos^2 \phi} = \dfrac{1}{\cos^2 \phi} - 1$ so $\cos^2 \phi = \dfrac{1}{1 + \tan^2 \phi}$

As $\tan \phi = \dfrac{r\omega^2}{g}$, then $\cos \phi = \dfrac{1}{\sqrt{1 + \dfrac{r^2 \omega^4}{g^2}}}$

(i) Resolving (H) and (V), and dividing $\dfrac{T \sin \phi}{T \cos \phi} = \dfrac{mv^2/r}{mg}$ so $\tan \phi = \dfrac{v^2}{rg}$

Therefore $v = \sqrt{rg \tan \phi}$

(j) $a = \dfrac{v^2}{r}$, so $r = \dfrac{v^2}{a}$. Hence $t_p = \dfrac{2\pi r}{v} = \dfrac{2\pi v^2}{v \, a} = \dfrac{2\pi v}{a}$

19 Vertical circles

(a) Acceleration is ↑ towards centre. $N - W = ma$, so $N = W + ma$

(b) $N = W + ma = mg + \dfrac{mu^2}{r} = m\left(g + \dfrac{u^2}{r}\right)$

(c) Acceleration is ↓ towards centre. $W - N = ma$, so $N = W - ma$

(d) $N = W - ma = mg - \dfrac{mv^2}{r} = m\left(g - \dfrac{v^2}{r}\right)$

(e) $N = mg - \dfrac{mv^2}{r}$, but $\frac{1}{2}mv^2 = \frac{1}{2}mu^2 - 2mgr$, so $mv^2 = mu^2 - 4gr$

$N = mg - \dfrac{mu^2 - 4mgr}{r} = mg - \left(\dfrac{mu^2}{r} - 4mg\right) = 5mg - \dfrac{mu^2}{r}$

(f) Using (d) with $N = 0$, $mg = \dfrac{mv^2}{r}$, so $v^2 = gr$ and $v = \sqrt{gr}$

(g) Using (e) with $N = 0$, $5mg = \dfrac{mu^2}{r}$, so $u^2 = 5gr$ and $u = \sqrt{5gr}$

20 Simple pendulum

(a) $x = l\theta$ From the definition of the radian.

(b) $60° = 60 \times \dfrac{2\pi}{360} = 1.047$ rad So, $x = l\theta = 30$ cm $\times 1.047 = 31.4$ cm

(c) Resultant force perpendicular to string has magnitude $=$ component of weight perpendicular to string $= mg \sin \theta$

(d) $ma = -mg \sin \theta$ so $a = -g \sin \theta$

(e) $a = -g \sin \theta \approx -g\theta$

(f) $\theta = \dfrac{x}{l}$ so $a \approx -g\theta = -\dfrac{gx}{l}$

(g) $a = -\dfrac{g}{l}x$ so if $a = -\omega^2 x$ then $\omega^2 = \dfrac{g}{l}$

21 Electromagnetic induction – moving wire

(a) $A = Lw = Lut$

(b) $BA = BLut$

(c) $\dfrac{\mathrm{d}(BA)}{\mathrm{d}t} = \dfrac{BA}{t} = BLu$

(d) $V = \dfrac{\mathrm{d}(BA)}{\mathrm{d}t} = BLu$

(e) Force $F_B = quB$

(f) Electric field $E = \dfrac{\text{Force}}{q} = uB$

(g) $V = EL = (uB)L = BLu$ – i.e. the same as part (d)

22 Electromagnetic induction – rotating coil

(a) $\phi = BA = BA_0 \cos \omega t$

(b) $\varepsilon = -N\dfrac{d\phi}{dt} = -N\dfrac{d}{dt}(BA_0 \cos \omega t) = -NBA_0 \dfrac{d}{dt}\cos \omega t$

$$= NBA_0 \omega \sin \omega t$$

(c) maximum value $\sin \omega t$ can take is 1, so $\varepsilon_{\max} = NBA_0 \omega$

(d)
$$\varepsilon^2 = N^2 B^2 A_0^2 \omega^2 \sin^2 \omega t$$

$$\left(\varepsilon^2\right)_{\text{mean}} = N^2 B^2 A_0^2 \omega^2 \left(\sin^2 \omega t\right)_{\text{mean}} = N^2 B^2 A_0^2 \omega^2 \times \tfrac{1}{2}$$

$$\sqrt{(\varepsilon^2)_{\text{mean}}} = \varepsilon_{\text{rms}} = NBA_0 \omega \times \sqrt{0.5} = \dfrac{1}{\sqrt{2}} NBA_0 \omega \quad \text{hence,}$$

$$\varepsilon_{\text{rms}} = \dfrac{1}{\sqrt{2}} \varepsilon_{\max}$$

23 Energy and fields – accelerator

(a) $p = mv = m\sqrt{\dfrac{2K}{m}} = \sqrt{2mK} = \sqrt{2mqV}$

(b) $v = \sqrt{\dfrac{2K}{m}} = \sqrt{\dfrac{2qV}{m}}$

(c) $v = \sqrt{\dfrac{2K}{m}} = \sqrt{\dfrac{2}{m}\left(\dfrac{mu^2}{2} + qV\right)} = \sqrt{u^2 + \dfrac{2qV}{m}}$

(d) $\Delta K = FL = qEL$

(e) $E = \dfrac{F}{q} = \dfrac{\Delta K}{qL} = \dfrac{V}{L}$

(f) $p = mv = m\sqrt{\dfrac{2K}{m}} = \sqrt{2mK} = \sqrt{2mqV} = \sqrt{2mqEL}$

(g) $\lambda = \dfrac{h}{p} = \dfrac{h}{mv} = \dfrac{h}{m\sqrt{2K/m}} = \dfrac{h}{\sqrt{2Km}} = \dfrac{h}{\sqrt{2mqV}}$

24 Energy and fields – relativistic accelerator

(a) $\gamma = \dfrac{E}{mc^2} = \dfrac{K + mc^2}{mc^2} = \dfrac{K}{mc^2} + 1 = \dfrac{qV}{mc^2} + 1$

(b) $\gamma^{-2} = 1 - \dfrac{v^2}{c^2}$ so $\dfrac{v}{c} = \sqrt{1 - \gamma^{-2}}$ and $v = c\sqrt{1 - \gamma^{-2}}$

(c) $v = c\sqrt{1 - \gamma^{-2}} = c\sqrt{1 - \left(1 + \dfrac{qV}{mc^2}\right)^{-2}}$

(d) $p^2 = \gamma^2 m^2 v^2 = \dfrac{m^2 c^2 \left(v^2/c^2\right)}{1 - v^2/c^2} = \dfrac{m^2 c^2 \left(v^2/c^2 - 1 + 1\right)}{1 - v^2/c^2}$

$\qquad = -m^2 c^2 + \dfrac{m^2 c^2}{1 - v^2/c^2} = -m^2 c^2 + \gamma^2 m^2 c^2$

$\qquad$ therefore $p^2 c^2 = -m^2 c^4 + \gamma^2 m^2 c^4 = E^2 - m^2 c^4$

(e) $p^2 = \dfrac{E^2}{c^2} - m^2 c^2 = \dfrac{\left(K + mc^2\right)^2 - m^2 c^4}{c^2} = \dfrac{K^2 + 2Kmc^2}{c^2}$

$\qquad = \dfrac{K^2}{c^2} + 2Km = \dfrac{q^2 V^2}{c^2} + 2qVm$

25 Energy and fields – closest approach

(a) $U = qV = \dfrac{Qq}{4\pi\epsilon_0 r}$, so $r = \dfrac{Qq}{4\pi\epsilon_0 U}$

(b) $r = \dfrac{Qq}{4\pi\epsilon_0 U}$ and $U = \dfrac{mv^2}{2}$, so $r = \dfrac{Qq}{4\pi\epsilon_0}\dfrac{2}{mv^2} = \dfrac{Qq}{2\pi\epsilon_0 mv^2}$

(c) $r = \dfrac{Qq}{4\pi\epsilon_0 U}$ and $U = \dfrac{3k_B T}{2}$, so $r = \dfrac{Qq}{4\pi\epsilon_0}\dfrac{2}{3k_B T} = \dfrac{Qq}{6\pi\epsilon_0 k_B T}$

26 Orbits

(1a) Newton's Second Law: $m\dfrac{v^2}{r} = \dfrac{GMm}{r^2}$ so $v^2 = \dfrac{GM}{r}$

(1b) From (a) $v^2 = \dfrac{GM}{r}$ We also know $v = \dfrac{2\pi r}{T}$ so $v^2 = \dfrac{4\pi^2 r^2}{T^2}$

Therefore $\dfrac{GM}{r} = \dfrac{4\pi^2 r^2}{T^2}$ and so $4\pi^2 r^3 = GMT^2$

(1c) From (b) $\dfrac{r^3}{T^2} = \dfrac{GM}{4\pi^2}$

(2a) Newton's Second Law: $m\dfrac{v^2}{r} = qvB$ so $r = \dfrac{mv}{Bq}$

27   Vectors and fields – between a planet and a moon

(a) $\quad F_M = mg_M = +\dfrac{GM_M m}{r_M^2}$

(b) $\quad F_P = mg_P = -\dfrac{GM_P m}{r_P^2}$

(c) $\quad F = F_M + F_P = +\dfrac{GM_M m}{r_M^2} - \dfrac{GM_P m}{r_P^2}$

(d) $\quad g = \dfrac{F}{m} = +\dfrac{GM_M}{r_M^2} - \dfrac{GM_P}{r_P^2}$

(e) $\quad g = 0$ so $\dfrac{GM_M}{r_M^2} = \dfrac{GM_P}{r_P^2}$ therefore $\dfrac{M_M}{r_M^2} = \dfrac{M_P}{r_P^2}$ and $\dfrac{r_P}{r_M} = \sqrt{\dfrac{M_P}{M_M}}$

28   Vectors and fields – electric deflection

(a) $\quad a_y = \dfrac{F_E}{m} = \dfrac{qE}{m} = \dfrac{qV}{dm}$

(b) $\quad s_y = \dfrac{1}{2}\left(\dfrac{qV}{dm}\right)t^2 = \dfrac{1}{2}\left(\dfrac{qV}{dm}\right)\left(\dfrac{s_x}{v_x}\right)^2 = \dfrac{qV s_x^2}{2dm v_x^2}$

(c) $\quad \theta = \tan^{-1}\left(\dfrac{v_y}{v_x}\right) = \tan^{-1}\left(\dfrac{a_y t}{v_x}\right) = \tan^{-1}\left(\dfrac{qV s_x}{dm v_x^2}\right)$

(d) $\quad s_y = \dfrac{1}{2}\left(\dfrac{qE}{m}\right)t^2 = \dfrac{qE t^2}{2m}$

(e) $\quad \theta = \tan^{-1}\left(\dfrac{a_y t}{v_x}\right) = \tan^{-1}\left(\dfrac{qE t}{m v_x}\right)$

29 Vectors and fields – helix in magnetic field

(a) $F = ma$, so $qv_\perp B = \dfrac{mv_\perp^2}{r}$ and $qvB\sin\theta = \dfrac{mv^2\sin^2\theta}{r}$.

Rearranging gives $r = \dfrac{mv\sin\theta}{qB}$

(b) From a): $r = \dfrac{mv\sin\theta}{qB}$ and $v_\perp = \dfrac{2\pi r}{T} = v\sin\theta$.

So $r = \dfrac{mv\sin\theta}{qB} = \dfrac{T}{2\pi}v\sin\theta$. Therefore $T = \dfrac{2\pi m}{qB}$

(c) $v_\perp^2 + v_\parallel^2 = v^2\sin^2\theta + v^2\cos^2\theta = v^2\left(\sin^2\theta + \cos^2\theta\right) = v^2$.

Thus $v = \sqrt{v_\perp^2 + v_\parallel^2}$.

(d) From c): $T = \dfrac{2\pi m}{qB}$ and $s_p = v_\parallel T = v\cos\theta\dfrac{2\pi m}{qB}$.

Re-arranging gives $q/m = \dfrac{2\pi}{B}v\cos\theta s_p$.

30 Vectors and fields – mass spectrometer

(a) $F_B = ma$ so $Bqv = \dfrac{mv^2}{r}$. Rearranging gives $r = \dfrac{mv}{Bq}$

(b) $qV_a = \tfrac{1}{2}mv^2$ so $v = \sqrt{\dfrac{2qV_a}{m}}$. Now using our result for r from (a),

$r = \dfrac{mv}{Bq} = \dfrac{m}{Bq}\sqrt{\dfrac{2qV_a}{m}} = \sqrt{\dfrac{2mV_a}{B^2q}}$

(c) From (a): $r = \dfrac{mv}{Bq}$ so $\dfrac{q}{m} = \dfrac{v}{Br}$

(d) From (b): $r^2 = \dfrac{2mV_a}{B^2q}$ so $\dfrac{q}{m} = \dfrac{2V_a}{B^2r^2}$

(e) $F_E = F_B$ so $qE = qvB$ and $E = vB$. So $V_s = Ed = vBd$

31 Deriving kinetic theory

(A) $V = l_x l_y l_z$

(B) $\Delta p = -mu - mu = -2mu$

(C) $F_{\text{particle}} = \dfrac{\Delta p}{\Delta t} = -\dfrac{2mu}{\Delta t}$

(D) $F_{\text{wall}} = -F_{\text{particle}} = \dfrac{2mu}{\Delta t}$

(E) Using velocity $= \dfrac{\text{displacement}}{\text{time}}$, time $= \dfrac{\text{displacement}}{\text{velocity}}$, $\Delta t = \dfrac{2l_x}{u}$

(F) $F_{\text{wall}} = \dfrac{2mu}{2l_x/u} = \dfrac{mu^2}{l_x}$

(G) a) $P_1 = \dfrac{F_{\text{wall}}}{l_y l_z} = \dfrac{mu^2}{l_x l_y l_z}$ b) $V = l_x l_y l_z$ so $P_1 = \dfrac{mu^2}{V}$

(H) No, as v and w do not change in the collision

(I) $P_2 = \dfrac{mu_2^2}{V}$

(J) $P = P_1 + P_2 + \ldots = \dfrac{mu_1^2}{V} + \dfrac{mu_2^2}{V} + \ldots = \dfrac{m}{V}\left(u_1^2 + u_2^2 + \ldots\right)$

(K) $\overline{u^2} = \dfrac{u_1^2 + u_2^2 + u_3^2 + \ldots + u_N^2}{N}$

(L) $\dfrac{PV}{m} = u_1^2 + u_2^2 + \ldots = N\overline{u^2}$ so $P = \dfrac{Nm\overline{u^2}}{V}$

(M) a) $\overline{v^2} = \dfrac{v_1^2 + v_2^2 + v_3^2 + \ldots}{N}$ b) $\overline{w^2} = \dfrac{w_1^2 + w_2^2 + w_3^2 + \ldots}{N}$

(N) $P = \dfrac{Nm}{V}\overline{v^2}$ using y components of velocity on back wall

$P = \dfrac{Nm}{V}\overline{w^2}$ using z components of velocity on top wall

(O) $\overline{c^2} = \dfrac{c_1^2 + c_2^2 + \ldots}{N} = \dfrac{(u_1^2 + v_1^2 + w_1^2) + (u_2^2 + v_2^2 + w_2^2) + \ldots}{N}$

$= \dfrac{u_1^2 + u_2^2 + \ldots}{N} + \dfrac{v_1^2 + v_2^2 + \ldots}{N} + \dfrac{w_1^2 + w_2^2 + \ldots}{N}$

$= \overline{u^2} + \overline{v^2} + \overline{w^2}$

(P) $\quad \overline{u^2} = \dfrac{PV}{Nm} = \overline{v^2} = \overline{w^2}$ so $\overline{c^2} = \overline{u^2} + \overline{v^2} + \overline{w^2} = \dfrac{3PV}{Nm}$ and so

$$PV = \dfrac{Nm\overline{c^2}}{3}$$

32 Gas laws, density and kinetic energy

(a) $\quad PV = nRT$ and $n = \dfrac{M}{M_M}$ so $PV = \dfrac{MRT}{M_M}$ and $P = \dfrac{MRT}{M_M V}$

(b) From (a) $V = \dfrac{MRT}{M_M P}$ so $\rho = \dfrac{M}{V} = \dfrac{M}{MRT/M_M P} = \dfrac{M_M P}{RT}$

(c) $\quad \rho = \dfrac{M}{V} = \dfrac{Nm}{V} = \dfrac{Nm}{Nk_B T/P} = \dfrac{mP}{k_B T}$

(d) $\quad PV = \dfrac{Nm\overline{c^2}}{3}$ so $P = \dfrac{Nm}{V} \cdot \dfrac{\overline{c^2}}{3} = \dfrac{\rho \overline{c^2}}{3}$ and $\rho = \dfrac{3P}{\overline{c^2}}$

(e) $\quad PV = Nk_B T = \tfrac{1}{3}Nm\overline{c^2}$ so $m\overline{c^2} = 3k_B T$ and $\overline{K} = \dfrac{m\overline{c^2}}{2} = \dfrac{3k_B T}{2}$

33 Capacitors and resistors

(a) $\quad Q = CV_0 e^{-t/RC}$ (or $Q_0 e^{-t/RC}$)

(b) $\quad Q = CV_0(1 - e^{-t/RC})$ or $Q_0(1 - e^{-t/RC})$

(c) $\quad Q_0/V_0 = C$ so $Q_0 = CV_0$

(d) $\quad V_R = V_C = V_0 e^{-t/RC}$

(e) $\quad V_R = V_0 - V_C = V_0 e^{-t/RC}$ i.e. the same as when discharging

(f) $\quad Q = CV_C = CV_R = C(IR) = I \times RC$

(g) $\quad Q = -RC\dfrac{dQ}{dt}$ so the differential equation is $\dfrac{dQ}{dt} = \dfrac{-Q}{RC}$

(h) $\quad I_0 = \dfrac{V_0}{R}$

(i) $\quad I_0 = \dfrac{(Q_0/C)}{R} = \dfrac{Q_0}{RC}$

(j) $\quad$ Time to discharge at constant current $= \dfrac{Q_0}{I_0} = RC$

(k) $\quad t = RC$, so $\dfrac{Q}{Q_0} = e^{-1} = 0.37$

34 Exponential attenuation with distance

(a) $I = I_0 e^{-\mu x}$, so $\dfrac{I}{I_0} = e^{-\mu x}$ and $\ln\left(\dfrac{I}{I_0}\right) = -\mu x$. So $x = -\dfrac{1}{\mu}\ln\left(\dfrac{I}{I_0}\right)$

(b) $\frac{1}{2}I_0 = I_0 e^{-\mu x_{1/2}}$ so $\ln\frac{1}{2} = -\mu x_{1/2}$ and $x_{1/2} = -\frac{1}{\mu}\times\ln\frac{1}{2} = \frac{1}{\mu}\ln 2$

(c) From (a): $x = -\dfrac{1}{\mu}\ln\left(\dfrac{I}{I_0}\right) = -\dfrac{x_{1/2}}{\ln 2}\times\ln\left(\dfrac{I}{I_0}\right) = x_{1/2}\dfrac{\ln(I/I_0)}{\ln 0.5}$

35 Exponential decay – using logarithms

(a) $X = X_0 e^{-\lambda t}$, so $\dfrac{X}{X_0} = e^{-\lambda t}$ and $\ln\left(\dfrac{X}{X_0}\right) = -\lambda t$. So $t = -\dfrac{1}{\lambda}\ln\left(\dfrac{X}{X_0}\right)$

(b) $\frac{1}{2}V_0 = V_0 e^{-T_{1/2}/RC}$ so $\ln\frac{1}{2} = -\dfrac{T_{1/2}}{RC}$ and $T_{1/2} = -RC\times\ln\frac{1}{2} = RC\ln 2$

(c) From (a): $t = -\dfrac{1}{\gamma}\ln\left(\dfrac{X}{X_0}\right) = -\dfrac{T_{1/2}}{\ln 2}\times\ln\left(\dfrac{X}{X_0}\right) = T_{1/2}\dfrac{\ln(X/X_0)}{\ln 0.5}$

(d) $I = I_0 e^{-\mu x}$, so $\dfrac{I}{I_0} = e^{-\mu x}$ and $\ln\left(\dfrac{I}{I_0}\right) = -\mu x$. So $x = -\dfrac{1}{\mu}\ln\left(\dfrac{I}{I_0}\right)$

(e) $\dfrac{I}{I_0} = \dfrac{1}{2}$ so, using (d): $x = -\dfrac{1}{\mu}\ln\frac{1}{2} = \dfrac{\ln 2}{\mu}$